Gift of

Mt St Joseph

June 28 - 1952

THE LEGEND OF SAINT COLUMBA

BY PADRAIC COLUM

World Epics

The Children's Homer: The Adventures of Odysseus and the Tale of Troy
The Golden Fleece: And the Heroes Who Lived Before Achilles
The Children of Odin: The Dwellers in Asgard and the Sword of the Volsungs
The Island of the Mighty: Tales from the Mabinogian
The Voyagers: Legends and History of Atlantic Discovery
Orpheus: Myths of the World

Folk Romance

The King of Ireland's Son
The Boy Who Knew What the Birds Said
The Boy Apprenticed to an Enchanter
The Girl Who Sat by the Ashes
The Children Who Followed the Piper
The Forge in the Forest: Stories of Fire, Water, Earth and Air
The Fountain of Youth: Stories to Be Told, from all his books
The Big Tree of Bunlahy: Stories of My Own Countryside

Stories for Younger Children

The Peep-Show Man
The White Sparrow

Poetry and Plays

Collected Poems
Mogu the Wanderer, or the Desert
Thomas Muskerry, etc.
Balloon: A Comedy in Four Acts

Edited

The Arabian Nights: Tales of Wonder and Magnificence
Gulliver's Travels, by Jonathan Swift

Novels, Essays, Travel

Castle Conquer
The Road Round Ireland
Cross Roads in Ireland
A Half Day's Ride: Essays

The Legend of
SAINT
COLUMBA

BY PADRAIC COLUM

ILLUSTRATED BY
E. MACKINSTRY

NEW YORK
The Macmillan Company
MCMXXXV

To

GENEVIEVE GARVAN BRADY

in friendship

CONTENTS

CONTENTS

ILLUSTRATIONS

THE LEGEND OF SAINT COLUMBA

THE BIRTH AND UPBRINGING OF COLUM-CILLE

THIS is our glen, Glen Colum-cille, and it would be hard to find in the rest of Donegal a glen as rugged and as dark. It is dark with the great clouds that are nearly always above it; it is gray with the stones that are scattered through it, and you would not have to go far from it before you come to the bare mountains and the brown empty bog.

Far away from this is the plain of Meath where the Kings of Ireland lived and looked from their height of Tara across wide and deep-grassed lands. Far away is Meath and long ago it is since the Pagan Kings lived there. Long was that line of Pagan Kings. And the noblest of them who gave worship to the Sun and the Wind was Cormac MacAirt. You will understand what a great King Cormac MacAirt was when I tell you that his Captain was Finn Mac-Cool—Finn the pride of Pagan Ireland. He was noted for his insight and his foresight as well as for his bravery and his resourcefulness. His great wisdom had come to him in a way that only a few of his companions knew about. Once he had taken a salmon out of the River Boyne. It had fed on the Nuts of Knowledge that had fallen from the sacred hazel-tree. Finn had burned his thumb in cooking it and a bit of the flesh of the salmon had stuck to his thumb. Ever afterwards when he put his tooth to his thumb he could find out what was signified by strange happenings.

If Cormac MacAirt was the best King of Pagan times, and if Finn MacCool was the best Captain, the best of the animals was Finn's hound, Bran. So wise was Bran that people thought that she was a Fairy woman who had been changed into a hound. Cormac, Finn and Bran—the men of Pagan times had much to show when they had these three.

Finn went hunting with his companions, the Fianna, and many and far ways they went before they came to the Ancient Glen. Here they started a deer. It crossed the stream that divides our glen in two and they loosed a hound on it; only one hound they loosed and that hound was Bran. But lo and behold! when hound and quarry were at the other side of the stream, the hound stood still, letting the deer flee away. This seemed to be of bad omen for all the Fianna, for never before had Bran failed to hold her quarry. They crossed the stream, Bran standing stock-still, and Finn tried to rouse her to pursue the deer. But the swift and wise hound stayed motionless. Then Finn put his thumb into his mouth and put his tooth to his thumb. Thereupon the reason for Bran's unwillingness to hold the deer became known to him: in this glen would be born one who would cherish all creatures; this had been foreshown to the wise hound and she would not take the life of the deer in that place.

You may be sure that the Fianna talked about this happening when they were back in the King's halls in Tara and when they were in their own camp on Allen. They thought that the child would be born, if not in Finn's time, then in the time of Oisin, his son, and if not in Oisin's time, then in the time of Oscar, Finn's grandson. But the years went by and they heard nothing of such a birth. Cormac MacAirt died and was buried with his Pagan fathers, and with the death of that King the glory of Pagan Ireland departed. Cairbri, his son, had to strike at the Fianna: he battled with them and broke their power; and Oscar was slain, and those who were left of the Fianna hunted no more on the hills nor in the glens of Ireland.

Niall came to be King, and in his time Patrick was brought into Ireland, a captive from Britain. While Patrick was yet tending his Pagan master's swine on the hillside, Niall's son, Connal, went from Tara into the North to win a domain for himself. Here he came and took possession of the territory that came to be named Tir-connal. Now one day when Prince Connal was hunting here he raised a fawn in the Ancient Glen. Across the stream the fawn went, the hounds chasing it. But when Connal's huntsmen went to where the fawn and hounds were they found the hounds gamboling

3

around it—playing in kindness with their quarry. The hounds even held the huntsmen off while the fawn fled away. Prince Connal marveled at this happening and he questioned a Druid about the significance of it; the Druid told him that in this glen would be born one who would love and cherish all creatures.

Time went by and a child was to be born to the wife of Connal's son—Eithne her name was. Now there was a woman in the place who bore Eithne great ill-will. She had a dream, this woman. She dreamed that a great bird took up the body of Prince Felim's wife and tore it into pieces and scattered the flesh over the lands of Eirin and Alba, of Ireland and Scotland. So great was her malice that she went to Eithne and told her the dream she had. But Felim's wife was not made fearful. She knew the true significance of the dream and she said to that ill-willed woman, "I shall have a son, and his words and his teaching shall be spread through Eirin and Alba."

Eithne's son was born in the Ancient Glen, and at baptism he was given a name which means "The Knowing One"—Crimhaun. But because his favorite place for play was around a church which stood here, his companions named him "Colum-cille" which means "The Dove of the Church"—those who write it in Latin make it "Columba." And because of his birth here our dark and rugged glen was named ever afterwards Glen Colum-cille. He was born here five hundred and twenty-one years after the birth of Our Lord, in the winter-month, and his life was in the same era as that of the great Roman Emperor Justinian.

Now you might think that being so directed toward holy ways, the lad would have little of boys' gamesomeness in him and would

4

not be found in the playing or the sporting teams. But you would be wrong in thinking so. He was sturdy and high-mettled and he was as good at striking a ball with a hurley-stick as any lad of his age. Any of the feats his comrades did he could do as well. But he never went with them when they went birds-nesting; he never took the eggs or young out of a nest although he could climb to the hawk's eyrie on the high, overhanging cliffs of Tir-connal.

He came to have a full, rousing voice, and when he said the responses to prayers, or repeated verses of poetry, or sang songs, the words could be heard at a great distance. He was familiar with all kinds of people and was welcomed in all sorts of houses; he went to wakes and weddings and christenings. But wherever he went he brought a book with him and would read while going along. He had learned to read while very little: cakes were made for him in shapes of letters of the alphabet, and as he ate his cake he learned a letter.

Now his tutor, Crunichaun, had set his heart on making this spirited lad a leader of the people in war and statecraft, a prince who would be sound in judgment, quick in understanding, and firm of will. He never called him by the name "Colum-cille," deeming that to be but a childish name, but always by the name "Crimhaun."

His father was not sure what he wanted this young son of his to be: sometimes he called him "Colum-cille," but more often he called him "Crimhaun." His father had now made himself King of Ulster. He was always matching his son against the sons of his brother Fergus—the boys who were named Sedna and Loarn.

5

These two had made up their minds to be Kings, if not in Eirin, then in Alba beyond the sea.

Once, toward the end of a day, he and his tutor were coming from the wake of a man of the parish. Colum-cille had his book in his hand, but his tutor did not give him a chance to recite his lesson, for he kept talking to him about his cousins and about the great figures they were likely to make in the world. Well, in the very middle of his discourse, Crunichaun fell down on the ground in a faint—he was an old and sickly man. And thinking that his tutor had wearied himself and had gone to sleep, Colum-cille took off his own mantle and folded it under the old man's head and went on reciting his lesson in a full and a clear voice. His voice reached to a convent that was some distance away. Crunichaun's three daughters were there: in their cells they heard the voice; they knew it was Colum-cille's, and they knew that where he was their father would be. They hastened out of the convent to greet their father. And lo! he was on the ground, and there was no sign of life in him.

The maidens knew of their father's disease and how mortal it was. They besought Colum-cille to lay his hands upon him and to bring him back to life. He did this, and when his hands were laid on him life came back to the old man. He raised himself up, and then and there declared that nothing else except the touch of these hands could have brought him back to life. And in the presence of the three nuns, his daughters, he renounced the thought of making his pupil a leader in the ways of the world and he urged him to retire from the world and to live the life of one of the saints of God.

The next day Crunichaun went into the hall of the King of Ulster and told him that he should leave aside all thought of worldly power for his son. And hearing this said, Eithne, his mother, rejoiced. She had just been told of a vision that a saintly man who lived in the middle of the country had had at the time this son of hers was born. He had seen a golden moon rise in the north, and Ireland and Scotland and the Western World were illumined by it. And he had seen a silver moon rise in the middle of Ireland, and the middle lands were illumined by it. And Eithne had the certainty that the golden moon that Fineen had seen meant her son, and that his purity, piety and wisdom would lighten the Northern and Western lands. Felim was moved by the words she said to him and agreed to let his younger son go from the ways of the world.

His parents were reverential about this and so was Fergus, his uncle. But not so were Fergus' elder sons. They mocked at their cousin's wish to leave the world, the world that they knew and longed to be masters of. Colum-cille kept silence under their mockery. But at last their father was put into a temper by it, and he said, "When I leave you your patrimony, I shall require that each of you give Colum-cille a portion of it to build a church and school." One of the youths at once offered a portion of his heritage. The other paused and considered and made the offer only after a while. Then Colum-cille said to him, "If you, Loarn, had spoken at once, offering me what you have offered, your descendants would be Kings in Ireland. They shall be Kings, but not in Ireland." This was a true prophecy: Loarn's descendants were the Kings of Scotland, but they had no kingship in Ireland.

7

Fergus had a third and younger son. He had been drawn toward the deeds and thoughts that his brothers favored. But now the radiance that was all around Colum-cille drew him to his cousin; he offered up a prayer that he might become like him rather than like his brothers. Thereafter he separated himself from his brothers and attached himself more and more to Colum-cille. The two were close companions throughout their school time and to the prime of their lives, so that any history that is told of Colum-cille in those days has his cousin's name in it. Bauheen was the youth's name.

THE FIRST WONDERS WORKED BY COLUM-CILLE

WHEN Colum-cille went from home to advance himself in studies
that would prepare him for being a cleric, Bauheen, who would do
likewise, went with him. The cousins lived next each other in the
students' end of the monastery; their huts were of timber, and on
the other street were the monks' cells built of stone. The church
was in the middle: it was built of hewn oak, and thatched, in sign
of lowliness, with reeds; beside it was the hall in which the
brethren read and copied Latin books, and near by was another hall
in which the students received instruction. Beyond were the fields
which the monks tilled or in which they pastured their cattle.

9

No sound of war nor sign of disturbance ever alarmed the monks and students who passed their years in that monastery. It was on a headland that jutted into the sea; it was separated from the rest of the country by a great bog which only a few who knew the safe paths could cross. The King of Ireland might do this or that and the Northern Princes might found new kingdoms across the sea, but the monks and students in that monastery took no account of such happenings.

Often, standing on the headland, they talked about and wondered at a strange monster that used to disport himself in the sea beyond. By many generations of scholars that monster had been watched without his motions ever having been understood by them. Then Colum-cille, after he had watched them for a while, found out what they portended. He showed the abbot that when this monster (Rochuie they named him) spewed out of his mouth in the direction of the land, sickness followed and lasted for the whole of the year; when he spouted high in the air it signified that there would be great storms and much destruction among the birds; when he spewed out into the sea it meant that shoals of fishes and flocks of seals would come to great destruction. After Colum-cille had interpreted the motions of Rochuie, the folk were able to prepare themselves for sickness, for storms, for destruction among the birds of the air and the fishes and beasts of the sea. The abbot thanked Colum-cille for the knowledge which he imparted to him.

As a thank-offering he sent him a basket of apples from the monastery's apple-yard. But the lay-brother who brought the offering gathered from the wrong tree; when Colum-cille bit into one of them he found that they were apples of an exceeding bitter taste. "Why are these so sour-tasting?" he asked. The lay-brother explained the mistake he had made, and said, "We have taken every trouble with that tree, but still it brings forth bitter fruit. Now we will have the woodman cut it down and its trunk and branches will go into our winter fires."

"Let us visit the tree," said Colum-cille.

When they went into the apple-yard, the brother took him to a tree that was growing on a rise of ground. It was sheltered from the high wind; it had sunshine; there was abundance of sound-seeming fruit on its branches. "Its timbers will be good for our fires," said the lay-brother.

But Colum-cille, walking around that bitter-fruited tree, blessed it; he said, "I bless thee, and I charge thee by the graciousness of Almighty God that thou changest thy bitter-tasting nature into that which is sweet and savory." He made the sign of blessing on the tree, and lo! a fragrance came from it that was felt by the lay-brother who stood beside Colum-cille. Thereafter that tree brought forth apples of sweeter taste than grew on any other tree in Ireland. And this was the first wonder that Colum-cille worked.

But soon another wonder succeeded this. There was a place near by that was very dangerous to man inasmuch as demons had made a refuge for themselves in it, and these demons were the remnant of the band that St. Patrick had banished from Cruchuan Aigle. They had come to this glen in Tir-connal, and they had raised a mist so that men could not see into the glen. And the river that bounded the glen the demons had turned into a fiery stream so that no man could cross it.

Colum-cille asked the Master's permission to go there that he might strive to drive away the demons who were troubling the people. At first the master would not give that permission. But when he thought upon the wonder that the youth had already accomplished, he gave him leave to go to that place with one attendant, the lay-brother who had brought him the basket of bitter-tasting apples.

As far as to the fiery stream that bounded the glen Colum-cille and his attendant went. There they halted, not knowing what they should do. And it might be that Colum-cille and his attendant would have retired then and left that band of demons in possession of the place for another while, if one of them had not, overcome by his own ragefulness, begun the attack.

This raging demon plucked up a holly-sapling and flung it toward where Colum-cille and his attendant were standing. The missile went through the body of the attendant, slaying him instantly. Easily might one have been appalled by the power of the demons within their mist. But Colum-cille drew the sapling out of the prone body and flung it back. And behold! the mist lifted as far as the missile went and the demons in their ranks were revealed. Where the sapling struck ground it rooted itself and grew into a holly tree; to this day that tree stands—it has not withered, and even now it grows a fresh and flourishing holly tree.

Knowing now that the powers of good were beside him, Colum-cille blessed the stream, and the fieriness went from it and it flowed on as clear water. Thereupon he crossed. The demons fled from the glen to a rock far out in the sea. But when he had called upon all the powers of the saints and angels, Colum-cille commanded the demons that they go into the depths of the sea so that they might no more harm or affright men and women. Thereupon the band flung themselves in, tearing for their passage such a hole in the rock that a man in armor might go through it. They took forms of fishes—fishes that have to be soundless in their depths, not affrighting anyone, as they formerly did as demons with their roaring and screaming. They are there to this day, and fishermen often take them out of the water, but if they do, they cast them back again, knowing them for what they are by the marking that Colum-cille put upon them; each one is of reddish color and is blind of one eye.

Then Colum-cille blessed the land from which these evil spirits had been banished, and he made the glen a sanctuary so that those in need of refuge might come and live there and be safe from those who were in pursuit of them. However, the folk who lived in the neighborhood begged Colum-cille that he would make the stream, which had erstwhile been fiery, of such depth that only those who came by boat could pass it: they begged him to do this so that the glen might not be filled up with runaways and unfortunates. But Colum-cille would not listen to their plea; he let the stream run shallow here and there so that the weak and weary might have no hindrance in crossing it, but come readily into that glen and be safe from pursuit and attack.

Now he was back in the school, living in his bothie and conversing with the Master and his fellow-scholars. And from where they walked, they could see beyond the headland the island that is named Tory. All who lived in that far-away island were Pagans, knowing nothing of the Word of God. The Master would have some of his scholars go there: he would have them get to know that barbarous people so that one or another of them, when he would be ordained a priest of God, might go to Tory Island and baptize the people into the true faith. All were eager to go, and one and another said, "Which of us will have the honor of going one day to this place and building there a church that will be named for him?" Hearing this said, the Master told them, "As the boat draws near the island each of you shall cast his staff toward it: it will be for him whose staff reaches the island to return there and baptize those Pagans into the true faith, building a church there that shall bear his name."

They set out in a boat, six youthful scholars. And when they had passed the headland, first one and then another stood up in the boat and made a cast of his staff. Each staff went through the air as if it were a javelin hurled by a warrior. Only one of these staves reached Tory: the others struck the rocky islets that are around the main island. And when the scholars landed, behold! Colum-cille's staff was driven into a ledge there. Seeing it, the others acknowledged that he should have the honor of returning there one day and of baptizing the people and building a church that would be named for him.

The Chieftain of Tory was not pleased to see strangers come near his stronghold. In a rage he came toward them. He held in leash a hound of surprising size and fierceness—no hound that hunted the wolf packs in the glens of Ireland was so large and fierce as this hound of Tory was. The chieftain, Oilill, loosed him: venom-foam was dripping from his jaws. Colum-cille stood forward to protect his company. When the hound came to where he stood he groveled on the ground and fawned upon Colum-cille. Oilill was stricken with amazement to see his fierce hound make himself so tame. And then he went away and did no more to prevent the scholars from going here and there on the island and building themselves cells of loose stones. The hound attached himself to Colum-cille, followed him everywhere, and at night lay before his cell. Seeing his hound become so friendly, Oilill reconciled himself to that band being on Tory; he even grew friendly toward them and promised Colum-cille that he would give them land on which to build a church on the day when he should return.

HOW COLUM-CILLE AND BAUHEEN WERE ORDAINED AND HOW THEREAFTER THEY ENCOUNTERED CERTAIN PERSONS

THE time had now come for Colum-cille to be ordained a priest of God and for Bauheen, his cousin, also. But from what Bishop in Ireland should they receive Holy Orders? "We will visit the most noted of them before we decide whose hands shall empower us to be priests of God." They left the monastery and went here and there through Ireland; they visited this Bishop and that Bishop, but they went away from each of them without Colum-cille's asking him to ordain either of them.

"We have visited over a score of Bishops," said Bauheen to him after they had been a month on their travels, "and we've had much discourse with this one and that one, but none did you ask to ordain us."

"An ordination is worth taking trouble about," replied Colum-cille. "Now we are coming to another Bishop; he may be the one we are seeking."

They went up to a house. "The Bishop is in the field behind his team," the house-servant told them. They went into the field; Colum-cille and Bauheen saw a man with a team of two horses plowing a ridge. His clothes were covered with clay, and he was so earnest in driving his team that he gave no heed to the two who came near him. "Have we left all the others to come to this one for ordination, Colum-cille?" asked Bauheen. "This one is a boor."

"It is wrong of you to judge by the outside of a person," Colum-cille told his cousin.

They called to the man at the plow; so intent was he on his labor that he did not hear or see them. With his eyes fixed on the furrow and his hands upon the plow he went along the ridge. Then said Colum-cille to the servant who came to them, "Take one of the horses out of the team." The servant took the leading horse. But still the man went on plowing, his eyes fixed on the furrow.

Then Colum-cille prayed that it might be revealed to his companion that their coming here was not a vain quest and that the man at the plow had sanctity which he could impart when he gave them Holy Orders. As he prayed the man lifted his eyes off the furrow and saw that the leading horse had been taken from the team. And at the edge of the forest he saw a stag with his head raised to crop the leaves of a tree. He called and the stag came from the edge of the forest and submitted to having himself yoked to the plow. Then with horse and stag for team he plowed the ridge; when the last sod was upturned he unyoked the stag and let him go back to the forest. After this wonderful happening Bauheen knew that their journey had not been in vain: this Bishop was the one most fitted to ordain Colum-cille and himself. And the Bishop, noticing the two who had come into the field, welcomed them, and led them into the house and refreshed them. And thereafter he brought them into his church and administered the sacrament of Holy Orders to Colum-cille and Bauheen. Thus the two companions were ordained.

Thereafter they fell in with two wayfarers: one was a gambler

17

who had the marks of a spendthrift upon him and the other was a destitute man who looked as if he once had had possessions. Both wayfarers craved alms from the companions. Colum-cille gave to them, and greatly amazed was his companion when he found out what he had bestowed upon each.

For to the destitute man he gave only a penny while to the gambler he gave a whole mark of silver. Bauheen reproached him for doing this. "To the man who looked to be in such misery you should have given more than a penny, and to the gambler you should surely have given less than a mark in silver." Colum-cille replied, "Perhaps it will be shown to you why I gave the more and the less." They journeyed on; the next day they were told of a wayfarer who had been found dead by the roadside. To where this one was laid out they came, and behold! he was the destitute man to whom Colum-cille had given a penny and no more. Under his torn shirt was a girdle; it was taken off him and in it were pence and five marks in silver. "This man was a miser who kept himself in misery and starvation," Colum-cille told Bauheen.

They took the road again; they entered a tavern to refresh themselves and in the tavern they found the gambler. He was treating poor people who were there to meat and ale and paying for what they ate out of the silver mark. "This gambler is not a good man," Colum-cille told Bauheen as they left the tavern, "but he has thought for others besides himself; he has divided that which we gave him among others who are needier than he."

Then as they went along the road that was one of the five roads that led to Tara they fell in with a band of poets. When the chief

18

poet learned who they were he made a poem in praise of their forefathers, Connal Gulban and Niall the High-king, and then demanded a rich gift in return for the praise that he had bestowed.
But what the companions had to give would shame them to offer.
Said Colum-cille, "Come to my father's house in the springtime
and I shall have rich gifts bestowed upon you and your company; I
will bestow what my people are wont to bestow on a company of
poets."

But this did not please the chief poet; he became angry and
scornful. "Not another foot of the road will I go until I make a
poem about you, Colum-cille, that will make the race of Connal
Gulban hang their heads in shame. I will satirize you for a close-
fisted, grasping, churlish, inhospitable race who would let the poets
of Ireland perish from want on their doorstep." When he heard
such words spoken, he reddened and paled, his heart sank and his
stomach heaved—such shame came upon Colum-cille. The poet
made the poem and declaimed it, and it seemed to the companions
a poem such as all men would remember and the lines of it would
be used against their race until the end of time.

Then Colum-cille prayed that God would spare them and their
kindred from such scorn and mockery. He prayed with his eyes
closed and when he opened them he saw a shape that was unseen
by the other. It was his angel Axal. And his angel pointed to an
ancient burial place and to a cairn that was therein. He went there,
and when he moved away the stones of the cairn, lo! a golden
vessel that the folk of the old time had put with a king who was
buried there. He gave the vessel to the poets, and they were con-

tent and promised they would never repeat the poem that had been made in mockery of his and Bauheen's race.

Bauheen never forgot the miracle that had saved them and their kindred from the withering satire of the poets. And thinking upon it he would say that Colum-cille was likely to become the greatest of Ireland's saints. But if he heard him say it, Colum-cille would hang his head and say, "There is no virtue so fragile as mine; I have such affection for my kinsmen that I am weak in favoring them; I am too forbearing with them. And with poets I am indulgent because of the delight I have in their art and because of my covetousness of their praises."

THE UNWILLING ALMSGIVING

THEIR journey took them through the territory of a certain King. But we must not give the name of that territory for the people thereof would still feel shame over their King's doings. We will mention the King's name nevertheless: it was Congalach.

No two in the world could have been more different than two Kings who were ruling in Ireland at the same time—Congalach and Guaire. They lived at different ends of the country and they were each other's opposites. If the leaves of the forest were gold and the crests of the waves silver, Guaire would weary himself giving all that gold and silver away. But Congalach was such a one that if he ever gave anyone a worn-out mantle (and he never did the like), he would be likely to take the clasps off it first and then send someone to bring the fringe of it back to him so that he might keep it to give to another person—if it ever happened again that he would have to give something away. He was the most grasping, niggardly, tight-fisted, uncharitable King that ever ruled over any people in Ireland; folk were afraid to ask him for anything; if they did he would send one of his long-handed followers to take whatever they had away from them.

Now when Colum-cille and Bauheen, going through Congalach's territory, came to the shelter appointed for them they found that it was nothing better than a tumble-down hovel. On their way they had seen a sight most wretched: three naked and shelterless lepers standing in the rain. They had given them some covering and had found out that in this territory there was no one to give the needy clothing or shelter.

In the tumble-down hovel they waited for the provisions that should be sent them. But it was not until the very end of the day that there was tale or tidings of its coming. And then they saw a half-clad fellow driving a hairy, squealing pig: he came to where they were, a bundle of firewood on his shoulder and a pot held in his hand. He tethered the pig to the bush outside and he laid the pot and the firing on the floor of the hovel.

"King Congalach sends you this provision," said the churl.

He went outside and slaughtered the squealing pig and brought the hairy quarters to them. Meanwhile Bauheen whose office it was to make the fire and cook the meat had tried to light the firing, hanging the pot over it. The firing was no better than damp branches broken off an alder-tree, and the pot had a crack in it through which the water leaked. "Not with good will toward us has such been sent," said Colum-cille. "Nevertheless, let us do with this provision and pray that God count it as a charity to King Congalach."

The churl went away quickly, fearful, as Colum-cille knew right well, lest his master be asked to do something else for them.

He himself went to where the pot was hanging. "Well, let us light a wisp under it in the name of God and Congalach's good angel," said Colum-cille. He lighted a wisp of straw under it, and the pot ceased leaking and began to boil. They put the hairy quarters in and the meat cooked in the pot. Then they sat down to eat,

Colum-cille saying, "Let our feast be to the gain of King Conga-lach."

Night passed for those in the tumble-down hovel and those in the royal house. This morning King Congalach would go hunting. He sat down to trim the shaft of his spear with a sharp knife. As he did he heard voices at his door. He thought there were people asking for something, and he jumped up to forbid the giving of anything. The knife he dropped wounded his foot. But his rage brought him to the house-door. Greatly to his surprise he found that none of his servants were there. People had been there and now they were going away: turning their heads they grinned at him, three men with hoods over their heads. Congalach did not know who they were, but grinning faces was not a pleasant sight that morning.

His wife came to where he stood. Seeing the wound on his foot she begged him not to go from the house that morning. The people who had been at the door she had not seen, but when he told her about their grinning faces she said, "It's a bad thing that you've seen, and I would that you had some good person's prayers this morning." Her saying this only made him more set upon his hunting. The wound on his foot he had bound up; he mounted his horse and rode off with his hounds and his followers.

They came to the river, hounds and men. And behold! a raft was on it, bringing from the other side the body of a dead man, and the three who pushed the raft across had hoods drawn over their heads. Congalach's followers thought that this meeting with a burial-party was unlucky, and they would have the King go no further. But for all their pleading he put his horse across the river.

Colum-cille and his close-companion, Bauheen, happened to be on the bank of that river. As soon as he looked on the man who was crossing, Colum-cille said: "Here is one who is near his death, and unless he does some good deed within an hour I know not but that he will lose eternal life."

"What good deed has he time to do now?" Bauheen asked.

"A man can always give alms," Colum-cille told him. "I shall ask him for something wherewith to clothe and shelter the lepers we saw."

"Do not so," said Bauheen. "This is Congalach himself. He will have you flung into the river if you ask him for anything."

"Nevertheless, I shall ask him for an alms, and it is for his own sake that I shall do it."

He went where the mounted man came to land. Then the horse stumbled in a badger-hole and dismounted Congalach. He stood with blood showing on his foot.

"Blessing upon thee," said Colum-cille. But the King did not return the blessing nor speak to him at all.

"Bestow something upon us," said Colum-cille, "for God's sake and for thine own sake, Congalach."

"Eh," said Congalach.

"We are poor clerics seeking for something with which we can give shelter and clothing to the naked and shelterless. Therefore we ask something from thee, King."

Congalach's hand went to draw his sword. But his attendant had not given him a sword that morning. He shouted to the men that

26

were at the other side of the river. "Bring me a sword or a spear," he said.

"Thou hast many reasons for not being niggardly," Colum-cille said to him. "Thou didst bring naught into the world, and naught wilt thou bring out of it. And he whom God hath given great possessions to is under obligation to share something with those who are in want. God is wroth with him who is without compassion and who gives nothing to the needy. If thou wouldst read the Scripture, Congalach, thou wouldst find it written there that there is small chance of salvation for him who is without kindness or charity. Our Lord's disciples never refused anyone anything they had, nor did Saint Patrick nor Saint Brigid. Nor have I ever refused anyone anything."

"Be off," said the King. But while he was struggling to say something more, Colum-cille recited:

> *Hear me and heed, Congalach:*—
> *The goods that you prize are mist*
> *Shut in a sinner's hand,*
> *And closed up in his fist.*

"Oh, a poet are you?" said Congalach. He hated poets just as much as he hated people who asked him for anything. The sight of Colum-cille poetizing and asking him for alms at the same time filled him with such fury that he could not wait for the sword or spear that he had shouted for. There was a stone shaped like an ax-head in the river and he plunged in to take it up. He would strike him with that stone and leave him stretched upon the river-bank.

Congalach did not come up out of the water. "Run, run," said Bauheen to Colum-cille. "His attendants are crossing over and they will accuse us of drowning the King."

He took Colum-cille by the arm and hurried him along the bank. But they did not go far before Colum-cille's foot got entangled in the King's mantle with its purple cord and fringes. Congalach had flung it aside as he plunged in. "We will take this with us," said Colum-cille.

"His attendants will surely slay us," said Bauheen. "They will declare that not only have we drowned the King but we have carried off his royal mantle. Leave it down and let us be off."

"How can I leave it?" Colum-cille asked, and he gathered the mantle tighter to him. "This is the only alms I have had from Congalach. Nothing now stands between him and a harsh judgment except what I carry."

"But it will not avail him," said Bauheen, "for 'tis an unwilling alms; not of his own will did he give you the mantle."

"Say not that it will avail him nothing," said Colum-cille. "Whatever a man gives of his own free will, God will reward him for doing it. That we know. But I shall not be easy in my mind unless, somehow, I prevail upon Our Lord to grant that the alms which has come to me, although unwillingly put in my way, shall profit him as much as if it were given of his own free will."

By this time the attendants had taken the body of the King out of the river and had laid it upon the bank. Colum-cille, holding the mantle, and Bauheen, grasping Colum-cille's arm, looked back.

28

"When they bring the horses across they will ride after us," Bau-heen said.

Colum-cille stayed. Even while Bauheen was calling him to be gone he was looking toward where Congalach's body was laid. "They will surely slay you," Bauheen cried, "especially as the King's mantle is in your hands."

What Colum-cille saw was hidden from everybody else's sight. He saw three demons with curving claws in the air above the King's body. They were in readiness to seize upon the soul of one who had never done a charity to anyone: as soon as the soul left the body of Congalach they would carry it off in their outstretched claws.

Holding the mantle in his hands Colum-cille hurried toward where the body was. The demons above it recognized that he who was hurrying toward them was opposed to them, and that his was a strong spirit and one blessed by God. They screamed out, "What right hast thou to come between us and the soul of one who did no good deed in the world?"

"I have had an alms from him," said Colum-cille.

" 'Twill not avail him," they screamed. "He did not bestow it of his own free will."

"Know, O besotted demons," said Colum-cille, "that the good that God's servants get from a man in any way, the goodness of God would have it accounted an advantage to that man." Hearing such words said so boldly the demons lifted themselves higher above the body of King Congalach.

Then Colum-cille cast the mantle over that body. So great was the virtue that had gone into the mantle that the demons did not dare go near the body it covered. With screams they fled away. And when the soul left that body they did not seize upon it. So it came to pass that Congalach was saved (and he was the only one we have heard of who was so saved) by an almsgiving made against his own wish and will.

COLUM-CILLE AND THE KING'S DRUID

ONE day when horses were tossing their manes and racing across the plain for delight in summer, Colum-cille went from the monastery he had founded and toward the demesne of the King of Ireland, toward Tara. The King who ruled in those days was named Dermott: much about Dermott comes into Colum-cille's story, but here we shall say little about the King and much about his Councilor. Dermott was the last King of Ireland who had a Druid for a Councilor—the Druid who was named Bec MacDe.

Bauheen was no longer with Colum-cille; he had gone back to the north soon after they had left King Congalach's territory. And on the plain of Meath near where the King of Ireland looks over his deep-grassed lands from the height of Tara, Colum-cille had founded a monastery that remained for ages as a place famous for piety and learning. He had many monks under his rule there; he stocked the writing-hall with scores of books, most of them copied with his own hand. But we need not speak of this monastery nor of the thirty others that he founded in different parts of Ireland: other books tell of this work of his. Only of one of the happenings during his sojourn in that place do we wish to tell.

It has to do with the King's Druid. Colum-cille was friendly with him, although being a Druid he followed after the old gods of Eirin and kept in his mind the spells used by herdsmen, smiths, cupbearers, steersmen and diviners. Now Colum-cille went across the plain toward the height of Tara. Halfway between his monastery and the King's dwelling he met Bec MacDe. The Druid started like a timid hound on seeing him, and then came on singing one of the songs of Paganism, the song of Aofe, the Warrior-queen:

> *Rock, rock, my battle-car,*
> *Plunge, ye war-maddened steets,*
> *Spear, strike on shield and ring,*
> *Sing me to madness, sword—*
> *Lord thou and only love*
> *Of Aofe the Queen.*

Colum-cille smiled to hear such fierce words coming out of the mouth of the little Druid; he knew that he was taking refuge in this Paganism because he was afraid this day of his, Colum-cille's, Christianity.

Colum-cille greeted Bec MacDe kindly, and after a while they both seated themselves under the branches of a great oak-tree that grew on the plain. They could see the high mound that is called the Brugh, or Mansion of the People of Faerie. Bec MacDe knew about the folk of the Brugh: once they were called De Danaan and they lived upon the level ground of Ireland. But the people who called themselves Milesians or Gaels came into the country and overthrew them in battle, and ever since the De Danaans lived hidden from the eyes of those who were descended from their conquerors—they lived in the Brughs or in the Hidden Islands that were far out in the ocean. The Druids were favored by the De Danaans, that folk whose lives would last as long as the world lasted but who could have no share in the life everlasting, and Bec MacDe himself had all his lore from them.

"But tell me this, Bec MacDe," said Colum-cille after they had talked of the wonderful knowledge the De Danaans might impart, "have they given thee to know when thine own end will be?"

"They have given me that knowledge," said Bec MacDe. "There remains to me seven years of life."

Colum-cille looked down upon the Druid. He was a small, thin man with a bald head that was shaped like an adze, large eyes, a large nose, and a very large forehead. Also, for so small a man, he had a very deep voice.

"A man might do good works in a shorter time than that," said Colum-cille kindly, "and knowest thou for certain that thou hast so much of life before thee?"

Bec MacDe was silent for a space; then he said, "It is but seven months of life I have, friend Colum-cille."

"That is a fair space of time to do good works in," said Colum-cille. "And art thou certain there is so much time before thee?"

Then Bec MacDe said in a very low voice. "Thou didst once declare, Colum-cille, that I, the King's Druid, who never foretold what did not come to pass, should make two untrue prophecies. Lo! I have made them. I have neither seven years of life before me nor seven months. I have but seven hours of this day left me."

"And I, knowing that, have met thee here, friend Bec," said Colum-cille.

"I put away my Druidism and my Paganism; baptize me now into the Faith of Christ," said the King's Druid.

There was a well upon Tara to which the King of Ireland used to go after his arising to wash his visage in: to that well that was named Laech Lesc, Bec MacDe and Colum-cille went. And in that well Colum-cille baptized him who had been a Druid. Then the small, thin man put his head on the other's shoulder, and seated so the two conversed together for the hours of daylight that were left. And when the sun was setting across the roofs of red yew that were on the royal houses, the life departed from Bec MacDe. One came to the well and going back told of his death. Then King Dermott himself and all his household came to the

34

well: the attendants raised the body up and bore it up the slope to Tara. There, with much honor, they interred King Dermott's Councilor, Bec MacDe, the last of the Druids who gave counsel to the High-kings.

COLUM-CILLE AND A PRINCE OF FAERIE

IT WAS after this that Colum-cille, walking by the spreading waters of Loch Foyle, saw one approaching. But nothing could be stranger than the way he moved: he came across the water as though walking upon it. There was a glow on his face and something resplendent in his dress, and when he stepped upon the shore Colum-cille saw that his sandals were of gold. "The blessing of all the gods be upon thee, Colum-cille," said this strange comer.

"Who art thou?" answered Colum-cille. "Who is thy King? What gods are they in whose name you give me blessing?"

"Myself am my own King," said the stranger, "and in the gods of the earth I put my trust."

"If thou art a King, or the son of a King," said Colum-cille, "it is strange that thou shouldst come unattended to where thou art not known."

"There would be thousands with me if it were my pleasure to be attended," he answered, and with his steady eyes and open face and rich garments he looked of royal stock. "I am Mongan," he said, "and my place is in the Faerie Mansions and in the Hidden Islands."

Then did Colum-cille know that it was one of the Princes of Faerie who stood before him, one who had wisdom and skill enough to dazzle mortals. He, who knew the true God, would not be dazzled by him. And Colum-cille, too, felt an affection for this kingly looking person, and he would fain help him to a knowledge of God and to a practice of the virtues of Faith, Hope and Charity. The lives of such as he were long—longer than many generations of men—but when the world ended their lives would end and they would have no part in the Life Everlasting. Out of his affection for him he said, "Tell me, Prince Mongan, the lore thou hast."

"I will tell thee," said Mongan. He seated himself beside Colum-cille under a great thorn-tree that grew beside the spreading water. "I know the Hidden Islands," he said, "the fifty islands in the ocean; around them the sea-horses shake their manes and on them the trees are ever in blossom."

37

"Until to-day we have had no tidings of such places," said Co-lum-cille. "Who are the folk who abide in them?"

"Well-favored people, men and women," said Mongan. "Death or decrepitude comes not near them. Their flocks of sheep have whiter wool than have any flocks in Eirin, and their cattle are white but with red ears. Beautiful are the white flocks and herds on the smooth and flowery plains of the Hidden Islands."

"We have heard the names of some of the islands," said Co-lum-cille, "The Plain of Honey, the Many-colored Land. And you yourself, Prince Mongan, what special skill have you?"

"There is not a creature in the world, from the fly to the ocean-monster, whose shape I cannot take," said Mongan.

"Great is your magic-skill, O Mongan," said Colum-cille. "As for me, I have knowledge of Heaven and Hell."

Hearing the names of those eternal places, Mongan, the Prince of Faerie, sighed. "I have knowledge of Earth," he said, "but of Heaven and Hell I know nothing. What would it avail me to know of them?"

"Eternal life," said Colum-cille.

More deeply than before Mongan sighed. "Only as long as the world lasts will my life last," he said, "and with the world my life will have its end. And knowing this I have come to thee, O Colum-cille."

"What would you have from me?" asked Colum-cille.

"That you give me the sight of Heaven and Hell," said Mongan, "so that I may understand what is above and below the world that I know."

38

"The Almighty would have given me great power if I could let you have sight of these eternal places," Colum-cille answered. "I will pray to Him to grant me that power. Come to me here to-morrow, and if it be the will of God I shall show thee what thou hast asked to see."

They took leave of each other in kindness and friendliness, and Mongan went across the waters of the spreading Foyle and Colum-cille went to his little church in the oak-grove of Derry, and kneeling on the ground prayed all night. He prayed God to grant him the power that would let the Prince of Faerie see the place of union with God and the place of separation from Him. Never did Colum-cille pray so fervently before. And when day was breaking his Angel stood before him and told him that God had granted him the power he had asked of Him. Then Colum-cille went to the brink of Loch Foyle, and he saw Mongan coming across the water. He said to Colum-cille: "Hast thou kept in mind the promise that thou didst make me?"

"I have," Colum-cille answered.

"Then, of thy kindness and for the sake of the true God whom thou dost know, give me sight of Heaven and Hell."

"Put thy head under my mantle and thou shalt see both Heaven and Hell."

That Prince of Faerie put his head under Colum-cille's mantle, and lo! he beheld the Kingdom of God and he knew it to be filled with light and glory and melody. And he fell into a trance through hearing that melody. When Colum-cille raised his mantle, Mongan came back to the sights and sound around Loch Foyle. "I

39

could not describe the least of the glories of the Kingdom of God," he said. "And now, Colum-cille, permit me to see the nether place." Again he put his head under Colum-cille's mantle. Now he saw into the place of the condemned. And the misery and despair of those who were separated from the love of God smote him, and he cried out, "O Colum-cille, for the sake of Him whom thou believest in, win me back from this misery."

Then Colum-cille poured into him a portion of his own faith and hope. The dread of separation from the love of God went from Mongan and hope grew in him—hope of his entrance into the Kingdom of God. Colum-cille listened to and talked to him in all affection and friendliness. They sat together under the old thorn-tree while the sun rose to its height and then began to set across the spreading waters of Loch Foyle.

Mongan asked counsel from Colum-cille and Colum-cille gave it to him from his heart and soul. He counseled him to separate himself from the Folk of Faerie whether they abode in the Brughs or in the Hidden Islands, and to live the life of a hermit in the deep woods or on an islet in a lake or in the sea. Death would come to him before the end of the world, and his soul, instead of drifting away, would come to the Judgment of God. With his heart and soul Mongan accepted the counsel of Colum-cille. Then when the sun was setting over the spreading waters, he rose up and embraced Colum-cille, and Colum-cille bestowed his mantle upon him. Into the water of Lough Foyle he who had been a Prince of Faerie cast his resplendent garments and his golden sandals, and covered with the mantle of Colum-cille, its hood drawn over his head, he went into the deep woods and began to live the life of a holy hermit. Time and time again Colum-cille visited him in his cell in the wood and found him steadfast in his faith and hope and active in his charity. So Mongan lived, and it is not known how he died. As for Colum-cille, he lived for many years in his cell in the oak-wood near by Loch Foyle. This oak-wood, Derry, became for him the best loved of the world's places; he built a church there, but the sound of the ax clearing away the oak-trees to make space for the church and hewing out beams to build it with seemed to him like the sound of death-blows: every one of the thousand strokes caused him grief.

COLUM-CILLE AND THE POETS OF IRELAND

OFTEN Colum-cille heard from Mongan stories of voyages across the seas in the *Ocean-sweeper* which was the boat belonging to Mananaun MacLir, the Lord of Ocean. And he learned from him about the various peoples who dwelt in Ireland in the old days before the Gaels came into it. Mongan's own folk, the De Danaans, went to live in the Brughs and the Hidden Islands when their kingship was overthrown by the Gaels or Milesians, that new-come people.

> *Conquered by the bright-haired, ship-borne bands*
> *That burst on Eirin, striving for wide lands,*
> *The kingdom passed from out De Danaan hands,*
> *Then Danaan heads bowed down, and warriors, lords*
> *Swore with the kings upon the heaped-up swords*
> *For ever cast away, that they would be*
> *Names only of remembered majesty.*

He learned from him, too, about the heroes of the Gaels, whether these heroes were of the North and were the comrades of Concobar, Fergus and Cuchullain, or dwelt in the South and were the comrades of Finn, Oisin and Oscar.

While Colum-cille was conversing with Mongan or while they were apart, one thinking of the vision he had of Hell and Heaven, and the other praying in his cell in the oak-wood of Derry, something was happening at the other side of Ireland which was to have the consequence of enshrining together Mongan's and Colum-cille's names in the memory of the poets.

That happening took place in Connacht. He who was King of Connacht at the time was Guaire, and he was famed for his generosity and his hospitality. And in those days the poets went in companies; they would stay a portion of the year on the domain of some nobleman or king who had to support them for a season or two. So when King Guaire had a message from the Chief-poet of Ireland, Senchan, saying that he and his company were about to visit him, he prepared to receive them with his native generosity.

But King Guaire was astonished when he saw the train that approached him. For there were three times fifty senior practitioners of the poetic art and three times fifty juniors, and every man of them had a servant with him, and every servant held on a leash a lean and hungry-looking hound. And as they wound up the path that led to his house he saw that the servants carried game-bags in which were stuffed the prey that had already fallen to these hounds, the geese, the moor-fowl and the hares of his territory. And there were howls along the line of their approach, for the hounds of Guaire's people had had their ears and paws bitten off by these invading hounds. Nevertheless, Guaire stood before his royal house and received the company in a way that befitted his own royalty and his guests' accomplishments.

Still, he could not help noting that while Senchan himself and his chief masters were affable and amiable, most of the seniors and all the juniors were of another cast: the King thought that he had seldom looked on such a lank-jawed, black-visaged, surly, unruly lot, and he wondered from what folk, Firbolg or even Fomorian, the poets of Ireland were now being recruited. He welcomed each of them and had them all comfortably disposed. He made a feast for them and afterwards announced that he would have a great house built for them with kitchens and beds. Next day he gave orders to have his buildings enlarged. Soon everything was made ready, and the company of poets were lodged and provided for in Durlus.

It was the preparation of the beds for them that led to the first outcries among Guaire's people. For the poets insisted on having bolsters filled with fine feathers, and to provide them with these the necks and breasts of all the geese in the district had to be plucked. The people were put in a rage to see their geese all looking so chilly, their fine and warm feathers gone from them. And then after the feathers, the geese themselves went, for the servants thought nothing of driving off a flock of geese every time the poets wanted to feast themselves in Durlus.

King Guaire remained courteous and his people remained tractable. In four months, they considered, the company of poets would betake themselves to other quarters. And so they would have if they had not been made so content with King Guaire's hospitality. Senchan and his chief masters were for leaving Connacht at the end of the season. But they were overborne by the juniors and the main part of the seniors: for now there were rains and the ways were miry, while the hearth-fires at Durlus were cozy, the beds were soft and the meals were certain; then there was sport racing one hound against another hound or hunting in the district for what game was left there. They would stay for another season, they decided. Senchan was not able to deal with this new element that had come into the Guild of Poets, and neither were his masters-in-chief: the nine of them stood round like ancient and tired cranes beset by a mob of active, big-beaked, loud-cawing crows. And, "We won't leave Guaire's! We won't go until the nuts and berries grow," they all cried together.

When the people heard that the poets were prolonging their stay they began to murmur and then they began to clamor. For now they had to spend days from their own labor cutting peat to blaze upon the hearths of Durlus while their youngsters spent days along the shore gathering mussels and winkles and cockles to make tasty messes for the more crotchety of the poets. Guaire himself was beginning to be hard pressed, for now he had to bring a drove of swine from an outlying forest and slaughter pig after pig for their feasts, and after that he had to bring a flock in from the valley and slaughter sheep for them, and then he had to bring his cattle up from the plains and slaughter beast after beast for them. And always his milkmaids were going to the pastures and coming back with flowing pails for the poets' porridge, and always the churns were splashing to make butter for them. And so it went on until the nuts and berries had ripened, and were gathered, and had been eaten in Durlus.

Guaire and his people thought that surely now the poets would leave Connacht and seek the hospitality of another of Ireland's kings. Senchan and the seniors would go, but the juniors would not; they told Senchan, and they told the King when he came

45

among them, that if anything happened to cause them to leave Connacht before another four months were ended, they would make a satire upon him and upon his people that would be remembered in ages after—they would make the King appear as a niggard and his people as churls. So there was nothing for Guaire to do but bring another drove from the forest, another flock from the valley, another herd from the plains, and make ready pork and beef and mutton for the importunate company in Durlus. In every hut a woman sat by the quern grinding and grinding meal to make porridge and white cakes for them. So things went on. And meanwhile the poets' hounds fought with the people's hounds and maimed them, and since there was no more game running or flying around, they took to dashing or sneaking into farmyards and carrying off the goslings—aye, and the geese, and the ganders even.

Guaire was at his wits' end to know how to get the importunate company out of his territory before his own and his people's substance was wholly wasted by them, and to do this without making them so displeased that they would make satires on the King and the people of Connacht. He visited Senchan and had a good talk with him. Their talk mainly was about the delight of traveling through Ireland from court to court. But the King found that the Chief-poet was feeble, that the seniors did not support him, and that the juniors were all in favor of their staying another season in Connacht where the girls were different from girls they had known in other places. ("And they'll soon be showing how different they are, believe me, my lads!" the King said, but he said it under his breath.) They would stay until the beginning of summer, Sen-

chan said, and then he himself would present Guaire with a poem
in celebration of the hospitality they had received, and then they
would make the circuit of Munster or Leinster. The Chief-poet
indicated the form and matter that his poem in praise of Guaire
would have:

> *Now we must depart from you,*
> *Rightful ruler, upright King—*
> *You who've cherished many bards,*
> *You whose largesse all will praise.*

Guaire thought it would be pleasant to receive this tribute, but he
reflected that it would be a long season before Senchan, standing at
the turn of the road that led out of his Kingdom, would recite it in
valediction. Meanwhile, leaving Durlus, he had to turn his steps
from one side to another to get through the crowd of poets that
were making their way from the kitchens, each one carrying his rations in his two hands.

And now another person comes into the story. This person was
Maravaun, Guaire's brother: he was a hermit who lived on an
island in the lake. The day after Guaire had learned that Senchan
and his company intended to stay another season in Connacht,
Maravaun went across the lake in his coracle to visit a brother-her-
mit who lived on the shore. He found him in a rage most unbefit-
ting a hermit: it seemed to Maravaun that he heard him mutter
something like curses. "Why are you so angry, brother?" he
asked.

47

"My goose-egg, my goose-egg that was taken from me!" the angry hermit answered. "It is not often I have desire to eat anything as rich as a goose-egg. But I had come through a long fast; my goose had laid an egg and it seemed as if God had sent it to me as a reward, so I was about to eat it. . . . The curse of the Seven Sages on them that took my goose-egg!"

"And who are the plunderers?" asked Maravaun.

"They who would have taken the goose with the egg only she rose up and flew from me—a wise goose. You asked me who took my goose-egg—they whom your brother, the King of Connacht, is cherishing to the ruin of all honest, hard-working, and prayerful people—the company of poets that have been set up at Durlus. For my goose-egg is to be put in a silver cup before his lordship the Chief-poet of Ireland at a great feast that they are all having to-night. May the shell of it get into his throat and stick there, and may the King who keeps such roisterers in his territory be blamed for his choking and have such a satire made upon him that his head will be left as bald as my goose-egg!"

"I do not blame you for your anger, brother," said Maravaun. "I do not blame you at all." And saying this, he presented the fasting hermit with six heath-poult's eggs: he had intended to share them with him, but now he decided to leave him the lot and go on to his brother's royal house. As he went along he started to think of how he should deal with the importunate company whose stay in the place was so upsetting to his brother's rule. And by the time Guaire had greeted him, he had, with the clearness of mind which is a hermit's attainment, made up a plan.

48

That night King Guaire went to the feast which the poets were giving themselves. As an extra guest did not matter in the lavish household of Durlus, he brought his brother, too. The place was filled: there were feasters at the long table, the round table and the side tables. The Chief-poet sat by the right side of the King, and the feast began by his eating the hermit's goose-egg out of the silver cup that Guaire had presented him with. The hermit sat at the side table with a dish of watercress before him.

When the feast was finished and the harpers had played, Senchan made an oration in praise of Guaire's hospitality and spoke of the praises he would have ready by the time he and his poets were leaving the court, which would be when the summer season had begun to smile upon the land. He extended greetings to Maravaun, spoke about him as a poet and begged that he would recite some of his poetry to the company. Speaking as Chief-poet of Ireland he declared that if his request was acceded to he and his company would, in return, recite any poem of the first rating that Maravaun might call for.

For a hermit in a company of poets Maravaun was very ready-tongued. He stood up before them and repeated a poem. It was not the sort that the Great Bardic Assembly would approve of: it was artless, but good of its kind. Maravaun chanted about the apple-tree that grew over his sheiling in the wood, about his friends the foxes and the badgers who visited him there, about the blackbird that sang to him from the branch, and about the cuckoo that called to him from the ridge of his roof. And when he had received Senchan's congratulations, he said, "I beg that the Chief-poet of Ire-

49

land, or some one of the poetic seniors would recite a piece which I have not heard recited for a very long time—the opening of 'The Cattle Raid of Cooley,' or the close of it, or, what would please me still better, the middle portion, 'The Lay of the Combat of Cuchullain and Ferdia.' ''

After Maravaun said this a long silence ensued. The Chief-poet looked to the seniors, and the seniors looked to the Chief-poet. Then the seniors walked among the juniors and talked to them anxiously. There was a feeling of uneasiness in the great hall of Durlus. "What you have asked for," said Senchan at last, "is a poem dealing with Kings who are now forgotten."

"And therefore unable to give food and entertainment to the poets of Ireland, and to receive in return poems of praise in a mode approved of by the Great Bardic Assembly," said Maravaun in a voice very different from that quiet-toned one he used when he spoke to his friends the foxes and the badgers.

The red of shame came upon the countenance of the Chief-poet. "The poets of Ireland knew 'The Cattle Raid of Cooley,' '' he said, "but that was before my time."

"Senchan," said Maravaun, and his voice had in it as much anger as was in the voice of the hermit whose goose-egg was taken from him, "Senchan, what the poets of Ireland venerated the poets of Ireland should have preserved, and not having preserved it they should recover it. I claim the redemption of your pledge. In return for the poem I recited for you you will have to recite for me the opening, or the closing, or the middle portion of 'The Cattle Raid of Cooley.' And until you do this neither you nor your company can stay two nights in the one place. Go now and find the passages I have asked for, and stand up and deliver them in this hall a year and a day from this night."

" 'Twill be at a feast that I shall give for your day-and-night sojourn in my territory," said the King with his wonted kindliness. "And my servants shall give you and your company cloaks and sandals for your journey through Ireland. My blessing with you, Senchan, and you, poets of Ireland, and success attend your efforts."

The poets muttered as they stood up beside the tables. "Let us satirize this fellow so that he will have to slink back to his cell and never speak again as he has spoken to the Chief-poet to-night at the feast in Durlus."

But Senchan, hearing these words broke the silence that had fallen on them all. He spoke in a loud and clear voice to his company and said, "We can neither praise nor revile a person until we have justified ourselves. We can only do this by recovering 'The Cattle Raid of Cooley.' Let us leave Durlus at dawn, and travel east and west and north and south, and come together here only when we have found and can deliver the master-poem of Ireland."

East and west and north and south they went, and nowhere did they find the beginning, or the middle, or the end of 'The Cattle Raid of Cooley'; folk said to them when they inquired, "We thought that the master-poem of Ireland was in the memory of the poets of Ireland." The year was wearing away, and if they were not able to come to the feast that King Guaire would give, and stand up in the hall of Durlus and recite what Maravaun would ask of them, they would be disgraced and never again would their guild have rights and privileges; they would have to disband their company, and no one in Ireland would ever listen to any one of them again.

Then Senchan thought of asking help from Colum-cille. He was a poet and for the sake of poetry he would help poets—even poets who had failed in the trust given them. So the Chief-poet of Ireland turned toward where Colum-cille was.

That was in the oak-wood of Derry. He was seated outside his cell listening to the singing of his pet wren when Senchan came to him. "Blessing on you, Colum-cille," said the poet.

"The blessing of God on you, brother," said Colum-cille.

Then Senchan told him how it was with the poets of Ireland. Colum-cille knew the offenses of the poets, but he would not have them disgraced if he could help it, no more than he would have his own brothers disgraced. He bade Senchan rest in his cell until the morning and in the meantime he would walk by the water of Loch Foyle and consider what might be done to aid him and his fellows.

At the first light of day he came to the old poet. He told him to go to the tomb of one of the heroes of the Cattle Raid—to the tomb of Fergus. He told him to summon from his tomb the spirit of him who had been at the beginning, in the middle and at the end of the Cattle Raid of Cooley, and who had related all the story to the poets of Ireland away back in the old days. "I shall stay here and offer fervent prayers to God that he permit Fergus to rise from his tomb and speak the words of the master-poem of Ireland."

So to the tomb of Fergus the Chief-poet of Ireland went, directed thereto by Colum-cille who knew where it was from the ancient histories that Mongan told him. His son helped Senchan to find that tomb: it was marked by a high pillar-stone. For days the poet and his son stayed in that lonely place calling upon Fergus, beseeching him for the sake of the heroes whose names and deeds were now unchanted to rise and relate to them "The Cattle Raid of Cooley." Almighty God, through the prayers of Colum-cille, gave Fergus' spirit the power to do this: he rose beside the pillar-stone; so tall he was that the words he uttered were distant and came only faintly to the ear of the poet and his son. Then he put his hands on the pillar-stone, and leaning over it, spoke to the two that were crouching there: he recited the stories—story after story that built up the great story of "The Cattle Raid of Cooley," from the birth of Deirdre, through the fight between Cuchullain and Ferdia, to the death of Maeve. And as he told them Senchan's son wrote them down.

The voice mingled with the calls of the curlew and plover and was no longer a voice: this was as the twilight grew into the night. And the shape that held the spirit of Fergus sank into the tomb. But then "The Cattle Raid of Cooley" had been won back, and Senchan and his son, carrying the written tablets, turned their steps from that place.

Then did the Chief-poet of Ireland gather his seniors and juniors around him; in a while they turned toward King Guaire's territory. A feast was made for them in the house at Durlus. But they did not go to that feast arrogantly and clamorously. Decently they went in and seated themselves below where the King and his brother were seated. At the end of the feast Maravaun rose up and asked the Chief-poet to recite for them the master-poem of Ireland. Then Senchan recited "The Cattle Raid of Cooley"; from when the King's great candle was lighted until it burned down all listened to him in rapture. And into the last lines of the master-poem Senchan wove a promise that henceforth the poets of Ireland would be faithful guardians of the poem and would observe civility in all their dealings with Kings and people, and would remember always the hospitality of Guaire and the helpfulness of Colum-cille.

COLUM-CILLE AND THE SAINTS OF IRELAND

BEFORE they went to visit certain of the saints of Ireland, Colum-cille and Bauheen, his cousin, betook themselves to Armagh, that place that was consecrated by Saint Patrick and in which the bell that he blessed was still rung. It was on a Sunday, and they walked near the church that Saint Patrick had founded and in the grave-yard in which his close companions were laid. Suddenly the ground gaped, the headstones fell, the cairns crumbled. Bauheen dropped the book he was reading into a grave that had burst open, and when he scrambled down to get it, he was struck on the head with the broken arm of a stone cross. He tried to pull himself out by grip-ping a branch, but the tree was suddenly uprooted and fell down on him.

"Why doesn't he do something to give his companions quiet and peace in their graves?" Bauheen said when he got the earth out of his mouth.

"Whom do you speak of?" Colum-cille asked, drawing his companion out of the way of a yew-tree that heaved itself at them.

"Patrick," said Bauheen, rubbing the sore place on his elbow. "Are we not in his stead? And why doesn't he do something to give his companions quiet and peace in their graves?"

"If you knew what Saint Patrick will do for the people of Ire-land on the Day of Doom . . ."

"There," said Bauheen, as the branch of a lifted thorn-bush poked itself into Colum-cille's eye, "I knew you'd get it, too."

"Nevertheless, you must not belittle Patrick, the protector of the people of Ireland," said Colum-cille, and he made two long jumps and got out of the graveyard, Bauheen with three jumps coming behind him.

"If you knew as I know what effort he will make on the Day of the Last Judgment for the people of Ireland, you would not murmur against Saint Patrick," Colum-cille said when they were out of the graveyard.

"Tell me, then," said Bauheen, "what effort he will make for the people of Ireland on that Last Day."

"Some part of it I can tell you, but not all," said Colum-cille. "Harken, Bauheen, to what I shall deliver to you, and never afterwards let a word pass your lips in belittlement of Patrick."

Away from the place of gaping graves and crumbling cairns and breaking crosses they seated themselves, and under the shade of a well-rooted ash-tree Colum-cille told his companion this prophetic story.

"The men and women of Ireland will assemble themselves at Clonmacnoise . . ." Colum-cille began.

"At Clonmacnoise?" said Bauheen in great surprise.

"At Clonmacnoise," said Colum-cille decidedly. "They will do that in honor of the greatest saint living in Ireland at the present time—Saint Ciaran. The folk of Ireland will assemble themselves there on the Day of Doom. And to that place Patrick will go. Seeing him there the people will know him for their leader. Then Patrick will strike the bell that he broke upon the demons when he banished them from the mountain—the bell that is called the Bernan. At the sound of that bell the men and women of Ireland will crowd toward their leader, and lucky will they feel on that day, they who were truly followers of Patrick, who kept his feast-day with alms-giving, and who never belittled his good-will."

"Amen," said Bauheen.

"With Patrick we shall march, all of us," Colum-cille went on, "but we shall tarry at Crosa Cail until the latest of the late-comers join us. Then we shall all journey to where Saint Martin has his station. We shall join with Saint Martin and thence go to where the most holy Peter and the most holy Paul have their place. Guided by these two primal saints we shall make our way to Mount Olivet.

"Saint Peter, Saint Paul and Saint Martin will go to where Our Lord is enthroned. But Saint Patrick shall stay with us, the men and women of Ireland. He will be seated on a chair of gold above our throng. Summoning Saint Ailbe to him he will send him with seven bishops to the feet of Our Lord on Mount Sion."

"Tell on," said Bauheen.

"He will send Ailbe to inquire what will Our Lord has toward the men and women in his charge. Our Lord, when he has bade Ailbe welcome will say to him, 'Where is the Lightning-flash of the Western World? He is long in appearing before us.'

" 'What is Thy word for him, O Lord?' Ailbe will ask.

" 'Many sinners are with him,' Our Lord will say. 'My word to him is this: leave behind ere coming before Us all those who have wrought evil in their lives.'

59

" 'How shall I say that to Patrick, O Lord?' Ailbe will say, 'Thou knowest that he whom Thou hast named the Lightning-flash of the Western World is a wrathful and quick-tempered man.'

" 'Nevertheless, thou shalt take My word back to him,' the Lord will say.

"With trepidation Ailbe will salute Patrick and say, 'I have had converse with Our Lord, and He bade me tell thee to leave behind ere thou goest before Him all who have wrought evil in their lives.'

" 'It appears that I have not been given even the beginning of a welcome on Mount Sion,' Patrick will say. 'And you, Ailbe, have failed me in this.'

"Then he will speak to Ciaran, Cainneach and myself, and declare that all the people of Ireland, sinners as well as sinless, must be with him when he goes before Our Lord. He would have none parted from him until he had spoken on their behalf.

"He will send Munda to Mount Sion then, Munda who was his companion when he came to make Ireland Christian. It will be Munda's duty to remind Our Lord that a promise was made to Patrick on his coming to our land—a promise that he would be the advocate for all our people upon the Day of Judgment.

" 'You who come from Patrick are not negligent in reminding Us of the promise made to him,' Our Lord will say. And he shall tell Munda that his word to Patrick is that he will have to put out of his following all who wrought evil in their lives.

"Then I shall find myself beside the golden chair on which Patrick is seated, and I shall hear myself being directed to go unto

Our Lord on Mount Sion, but what I am being told to say or do I shall not be able to recollect, for the sound of all the waves of the world will be in my ears. I shall find myself standing at the feet of Our Lord, and when He speaks to me I shall be able to speak of one thing only, namely, of Patrick's great love for all the people of Ireland, sinners as well as sinless, the love that brought him to keep a long and wasting fast upon the mountain that is named Cruachan, to the end that no one born in Ireland after the coming of the Faith should lose utterly the friendship of Our Lord. And having said this there will be such silence that I will believe that sound has utterly departed from the world. And then I shall hear Our Lord make answer, and He will say:

" 'We will consult with the Nine Hierarchies of Heaven about what We shall do about this Patrick and his following.' And He shall say to me in a kindly voice, 'Go back to him, and bid him come to Us with the whole of the host that is his people. Ah, but tell him, too, that he will have to do this. . . .' "

Thereupon Colum-cille paused, and Bauheen, in great anxiety, asked him:

"What will Patrick have to do for the people of Ireland upon that Day?"

Colum-cille opened his mouth to speak. But at that moment the bell of Armagh, Saint Patrick's bell, sounded.

"That stroke is to remind us," said Colum-cille, "that it is fitter for us to be inside Saint Patrick's church, praying as Saint Patrick taught us to pray, than to be foretelling what he will do for us on the Day of Judgment."

"But what will he do for us on the Day of Judgment?" Bauheen asked as they went over the ground that was hollow and lumpy but no longer heaving.

"God decreed that the bell should be struck at that moment to forbid my telling what more the Lightning-flash of the Western World will do for the people of Ireland on the Judgment Day," Colum-cille said, and saying this he and Bauheen went into the church and listened to the hymn that was being sung in praise of Saint Patrick.

From Armagh they set out to visit different monasteries in Ireland. Of the greater part of these visitings there is no tale to be told. But what happened when they were in the monastic settlements of Ciaran and Enda has to be related in a Life of Columcille.

Ciaran's settlement was at the bend of the Shannon River. The place is called Clonmacnoise now, but then it was called Tiprat. This was not the only place that Ciaran had come to through his wish to live a life of holiness. He had been on an island in Lough Ree. There he had built his cell and planted a garden, and there he had waited for the coming of good men who would be his monks. One had come at last whose name was Donnan. But when Ciaran saw how this man delighted in the sights and sounds of the island and how the birds and the little creatures of the place made friends with him, Ciaran had said, "Brother, this place is for you rather than for me," and he had left the island to Donnan, himself going to seek another site. Along the side of the river he had gone until he came to a place that is named Ard Mantain. He had considered it as a place where his monastic settlement might be founded. But the next day he had said to himself, "Here there is abundance of all that keeps life in a man; my monks would not have to labor hard in this place, and so their road to heaven would not be a clear one; not here should my monastic settlement be." So he had gone from that place carrying on his shoulder his bag of books.

Going along the ways he had met a stag that, with his antlered head bent, seemed to wait for him. Placing his bag of books on the stag's back, Ciaran had followed where he led. Where the river makes a bend the stag halted, and Ciaran had known that this should be the site of his monastic settlement. Taking his bag of books off the stag's back he had blessed the creature and permitted him to depart. There he had built his cell, and, laboring the ground, had waited for those who might come to him. Many had come to him there, good men who, accepting his rule had become his monks. And so, in the place that was called Tiprat, Ciaran had his monastic settlement.

And when Colum-cille and Bauheen came to it, Ciaran had welcomed the two of them, but he gave Colum-cille an especial welcome. These two, the one a carpenter's son and the other a king's son and the great-grandson of the High-king of Ireland, had known each other before, and had admired and loved each other. They would sit together for hours making copies of the Gospels, Ciaran copying one half and Colum-cille the other so that their handwriting should lead from a page written by one to a page

63

written by the other. It was to Ciaran that Colum-cille addressed this little poem:

> Little horn, mine,
> Filled up to the brink,
> One is coming nigh—
> User of much ink.
>
> Lovingly he'll greet
> Me this bright, clear morn;
> Dip and dip we'll take
> From you, little horn.

They were sharers, Colum-cille and Ciaran. These were happy days for Colum-cille and he often thought on them in the dark days that came on him afterwards. And it is no wonder that these two saints of Ireland were happy sharing their goods and their minds and their hours with each other. They were of the one age, and it was of Colum-cille and Ciaran that Fineen had the vision when he saw a golden moon rising over the north of Ireland and a silver moon rising over the middle lands.

But Colum-cille was to go from Tiprat with a sorrowful happening touching him. One who was a poet and a man of learning came to see him there. Colum-cille talked to him in the company of Ciaran and Bauheen. Then when the man went from them, Bauheen said, "This was not like your way, Colum-cille; you used to have the poets recite one of their poems to you and the men of learning tell you something of their lore. But with this man you talked only of kings' designs." Then Colum-cille said, "How could I ask one who has great sorrow before him to give us solace? He who has left us will soon come face to face with a great misfortune." And so it turned out; as Colum-cille and Bauheen were leaving Tiprat next morning a messenger came with the news that the man's children had been drowned while he was visiting Colum-cille.

They took leave of Ciaran, Colum-cille and Bauheen, and with the sadness of their visitor's loss upon them, crossed the Shannon and set out for the monasteries of the West. Of several that they visited there is no tale to be told. And then they put off for the island that is beyond the Western mainland, the Island of Arran in the stormy sea.

It seemed to Bauheen that Colum-cille liked this far-away place better than any other place that their visiting had brought them to—Arran, the treeless island in the stormy sea. And Bauheen knew that Colum-cille wished that he could like Enda as well as he liked Arran—Enda, the Abbot of the monastery there. But Enda, that busy and severe man, always teaching and always ordering affairs, had nothing about him that would make people fond of him. And he was not one who could be very fond of any person.

As they were walking across the plain of Arran one day, Enda with certain of his monks and Colum-cille with Bauheen, Colum-cille said: "I would that I had some portion in your island, Enda, so that my name might be fixed to it." "It need not take much ground to hold a man's name, friend Colum-cille," Enda said. "I will give you as much of my island as your hood will cover." Thereupon Colum-cille took the hood off his head and laid it on the ground. "What it covers shall be named for Colum-cille," Enda promised.

The hood opened out; it spread; the monks had to run in all directions to keep beside it. It covered a field. Enda caught a corner of the spreading hood and shouted to his monks to take hold of the other corners. They had to run very fast to do so, for it went like fire in the grass. But when they lifted it up it ceased to spread. It folded into a hood again and Colum-cille put it on his head.

The fair, wide field it had covered had to be named for Colum-cille. But if Enda made the grant he made it silently and frowningly. Then said Colum-cille to all who stood on that field, "On some island like this I shall end my days: since I came here this

66

has been foreshown me. For this reason I would have rejoiced to have a portion of the island that would not be narrow and confined. And had you, Enda, not begrudged me this," he said, "well would it have been for Arran and its people! No ships save those bearing pilgrims would have come here. One man might have defended its ship-stead against all the ships of the Northern seas. He who had done a guilty deed here, his soles would have fastened to the soil, and he would not be able to put one foot past the other until he had repented of his misdeed. The water of the wells would have been mingled with honey, and a flock of the birds of Paradise would have sung here all day long. The bells would have chimed of themselves and the candles of the churches would have kindled themselves, and as for the hearths of the folk, they would never lack peat for the fires."

It is no wonder that the people of Arran to this day are sorry because of Enda's begrudgingness. They have no peat for fires for their hearths; they have to go in boats to get peat for their fires from bogs upon the mainland. It would have been different if Enda had been more open-hearted to Colum-cille.

After this Enda and Colum-cille and the company of monks came to a great mound. "What a pity it is we do not know who is buried here!" one of the monks said. Immediately Colum-cille was given knowledge, and he knew who he was who was buried there. "An Abbot of Jerusalem is buried beneath this mound," he said. "He sailed to Ireland before the Faith had yet been brought here, and he died here among strangers in this far place." He knelt down by the mound and prayed, and they all prayed with him.

It seemed to Bauheen that Colum-cille was greatly moved by the thought of the Abbot who had come there and who had died at such a distance from his own people.

That night as Bauheen was lying wakeful in his own cell he saw Colum-cille leave his and cross the ground of Arran in the moonlight. He followed him. To the mound that marked the grave of the Abbot of Jerusalem Colum-cille went; he stood beside it with his head bent. And when Bauheen spoke to him, he raised his head, and said:

"It was given me to choose the death I should prefer to have and the region in which I should pass a long part of my life before my end. I made my choice: I chose to die after the pride of manhood had left me and before the weaknesses of old age had fallen upon me. It is not possible for a man well gone in years to live otherwise than safely and softly. And I would be loath to have a soft life for my body. And I chose a long exile from my own country and my own home and fatherland, with death after long sorrow and great penitence. For a man is chastened by exile, and in that state it is easy for him to take his mind away from the vain things of this world."

He said this with such assurance of its coming to pass that Bauheen wept as he stood with him beside the burial-mound of that Abbot of Jerusalem who was so separated from his own land and people.

THE BOOK

AND now we come to speak of those dire happenings that led to Colum-cille's severance from his own people and his own land, and to his abiding for the rest of his lifetime among a different people and in another land. And we who write these words invoke the saintship of Colum-cille to the end that what we set down here may be to the honor of God, to the uplifting of the name of Colum-cille, to the lasting good of those who read these pages or harken to them being read, to the good of our own soul, and, finally, to the dishonor, confusion and overthrow of the Evil One. Amen!

From Arran Colum-cille went to Druim Finn, the Monastery that Finnen was Abbot of. He found Abbot Finnen all lordly importance. It was not long until he came to know that there was a double reason for the Abbot's open self-satisfaction. In the first place, the King of Ireland, even Dermott, was to visit his monastery on the morrow. And in the second place he had received a book from a monastery in Gaul, a book that no other monastery in Ireland had a copy of. It was no wonder that Finnen had this swelling pride in him. He took Colum-cille into the writing-hall and showed him the book; then he hurried away to make preparations for King Dermott's coming.

There were no monks at work at the writing-tables; no one was copying or illuminating pages of books; all were making ready for the King's reception. Colum-cille propped the new-brought book before him and began to read its pages. It was a book about the Gospels by one of the great Teachers, and it contained comments

and elucidations that should be made known to all who were bringing Christ's words to men. Long had the monasteries of the West
waited for this book: now it was here, in the writing-hall of Druim
Finn.

Leaves of parchment were before Colum-cille, and a rack full of
quills and different-colored inks. He dipped a quill into ink, and
began writing, copying the first page of the book that was before
him. He lost thought of everything except the need of getting on
a page the words that were on the page before him. He wrote on
and on, looking only from the page he was writing on to the page
he was copying from. As he wrote, the pet crane that used to follow him on his journeys flew in through the window-opening and
stood motionless on its long legs in the middle of the writing-hall.

The bell rang for the meal in the refectory, but Colum-cille
heard nor heeded it no more than did the crane. But unlike the
crane, he moved, his hand making lines of writing across page
after page of parchment. The writing-hall was darkening as the
sun went down. Then the crane moved: it was wont to fetch a
candle for Colum-cille when the darkness came and he was still
engaged in writing. It stretched up and took a candle from a shelf
and brought it to him. He struck fire and lighted the candle and
went on copying from the book; now page was laid on page before him.

The bell rang for the monks to retire to their cells. Then it
became known that Colum-cille was not among the brethren. One
saw a light in the writing-hall and told the Abbot of it. Finnen
hurried there. He opened the door. As he did, the pet crane that

was standing on guard struck with his beak. The Abbot's knee got a hard tap, and only that the stuff of his robe was thick his

knee would have been knocked crooked on him. He went hobbling and stumbling down the passage and away from the writing-hall.

But what could be going on there? He sent one of the novices to find out and tell him. The lad went to the writing-hall. But when he came to the door he thought before opening it. Then he drew back the little shutter that was in the middle of the door. He saw Colum-cille at the table, writing and writing away, the candle behind him nearly burnt out. He had only a second to see this, for the crane struck with its beak, and catching him below the eye, laid his cheek open with a gash. The novice gave a cry and ran down the passage to the Abbot's cell.

Colum-cille did not hear nor heed the cry, for he was now upon the last page, and the candle, guttering, was making shadows on the page. But he wrote on and on. And the novice in his cell was telling the Abbot what he had seen—Colum-cille copying the book that had been sent their monastery from the monastery in Gaul.

Abbot Finnen was put into a great temper by this news. With his seniors about him, he went into the writing-hall and bade Colum-cille desist from copying. But Colum-cille did not hear nor heed him, for now he was writing the last words and the candle was going out. Then the last words were written, and the Abbot and his seniors stood around him, speaking to him. He was so toil-worn that what they said did not have any meaning for him. He put all the parchment-pages together, and wishing the Abbot and his seniors the peace of the night, went to his cell, and lying down on his bed fell fast asleep.

He was awakened on the morrow by the jangling of bridle-chains as King Dermott and his attendants came to Finnen's monastery. He knew then that he had done something that he would have to make excuses for—he had made a copy of Finnen's book without asking permission. But Finnen would have to have the book copied and copied many times, for that book, long waited for, was needed in many places. He went from his cell and walked in the garden, and saw the King and his attendants going to the repast that was prepared for them. And he thought that in a while he would go and excuse himself to Finnen, and thank him for the opportunity of copying the book, and then leave the monastery, taking the copy he had made with him.

Then came a novice and summoned him to the presence of the Abbot and the King. They were in the writing-hall. And no sooner had he entered and saluted the Abbot and the King, than Finnen reprimanded him for copying without his knowledge or leave the book that had been sent him from Gaul.

Colum-cille took up the copy he had made and held it in his hand. "I labored that the wisdom that is in your book might be made known to men who have longed to know it," he said to Finnen. "I would have them come here to read the book," said Finnen, "and so have my monastery famous throughout all Ireland and the Western World." "That is not a worthy consideration," said Colum-cille, "and I am glad that I have this copy to take away with me." "You have not that copy," said Finnen, "for that is the child-book of my parent-book, and it must remain here." Then Colum-cille turned to King Dermott. "It is well that you are here, O King," he said, "for you give utterance to the laws of

Ireland. Is it not right that the wisdom that is in this book should be made open to many people?"

King Dermott shook his head. "The parent-book is Finnen's and the child-book should be Finnen's also: this is my judgment, and no other judgment is possible. You, Colum-cille, may not take away the copy you have made." "It is not a worthy judgment, O King of Ireland," said Colum-cille, "and I shall appeal to you on it: I shall appeal to you where you give judgment upon high issues, to you on your Judgment Hall of Tara. For know, O King, that this is not a small issue between Finnen and myself, but one affecting generations to come."

THE JUDGMENT

No SOONER had King Dermott got back to Tara than he heard of Colum-cille again, and again he heard of him in a way that was disturbing to his royal peace. Colum-cille's kinsmen, the Clann Conaill, had grown powerful and proud in the North, so powerful and proud that they gave scant allegiance to the King of Ireland. They had given support to the King of Connacht when he would have withheld the tokens of his subordination. That trouble had been brought to an end: the King of Connacht had sent a hostage to Tara, his own son, Curnan, and the Clann Conaill had gone surety for his good treatment. It was easy for them to do this, for it was a matter of pride with the King of Ireland to treat his hostages kindly and honorably. And now there was this disturbance: in a hurling-match between the youths of Tara, Curnan had struck with a hurling-stick the head of the son of the Chief Steward of Tara, and had left him dead on the field. Muttering to himself that everything that had to do with the Clann Conaill was difficult and disturbing, King Dermott ordered that Curnan be put by himself in a hut and kept there till the Chief Steward felt that he had had satisfaction for the death of his son. Then King Dermott sent for his lawyers to prepare judgment in the case that Colum-cille would bring before him.

The Chief Steward of Tara was an ill-willed and revengeful man. He took Curnan and put him in a hut that was at the outskirts of the royal demesne. He left him there, alone and in darkness, and without food or drink. This Dermott did not know. His lawyers were with him: he was delighted to find that they recommended a judgment which would be in favor of Finnen and altogether against Colum-cille.

A day came when Colum-cille went to Tara and appeared in the King's Hall of Judgments. Notable people attended that assize—clerics and learned men and princes and famous artificers; Finnen was there also. The proceedings opened by his laying claim to the copy of the book that Colum-cille had made.

There were two or three in the hall who felt that Finnen had not as much right on his side as he and nearly all the others thought he had, and the questionings of these two or three and the replies that the men of law were forced to give them, kept the proceedings going for longer than anyone thought they would go on. It seemed that the matter was not as clear as so many people had thought. The King's great candles were lighted and burned down, and still points were being mooted and confuted. Then as the dawn came and the wick of the last great candle flickered out, Colum-cille stood up in the center of the hall, and, holding the book he had copied in his hand, answered Finnen and the men of law. That resonant voice of his rang through the Hall of Judgments. "Finnen's claim would fasten a worn-out law on us," he said. "Books are things different from other possessions, and any law that deals with them should recognize such difference. And we learned men who have received a new heritage of knowledge— what should we do but multiply and scatter the books that contain this knowledge? I maintain that Finnen's book is none the worse for my having copied it. And it is right that my copy should

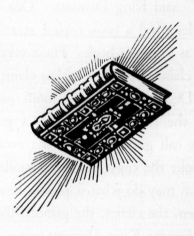

go to those who want to read what is in it and who are worthy to do so, and that they should make copies, too, and send them further. It was not wrong on my part to copy the book, seeing that there was no profit for me in my doing so, but only labor, and seeing that I had the desire to give profit to all the peoples of Ireland, and that without doing any damage to Finnen or to his book."

"We know naught of these new-fangled ways of talking about people's property," said King Dermott. "Our learned communities have always described a book copied as a 'child-book' and a book copied from as a 'parent-book.' These very terms imply that a person who has claim upon the one has claim upon the other." And then King Dermott gave his famous judgment from the Judgment-seat of the Kings of Ireland. "I go back to ancient precedent—'Every calf goes with its cow'; every child-book goes with its parent-book; the copy that Colum-cille made stays with Finnen, and Finnen may do what it pleases him with it."

The learned men, the clerics, the princes, the famous artificers applauded the judgment King Dermott gave. "A right-judging King indeed!" they said. "Only those who are willfully blind will refuse to see the aptness of it. The wisdom of the ancients is in King Dermott; he is a bulwark to us against all those self-seekers who try to profit by a change that is coming over men's minds to-day."

All turned away from Colum-cille; no one spoke to him as he went away from the crowd that had stood before the Judgment Seat of the King. The anger that Clann Conaill often felt about the

Kings at Tara flared up in him as he went down the slope. "These blustering Northerners have been shown that there is law in Tara," he overheard one learned man say to another. But who was this law-giver he said to himself? If the descendants of Niall the Great had their rights, it would not be Dermott but one of the Clann Conaill who would be in the Judgment Seat—perhaps, he, Colum-cille himself!

As he was about to go out of the King's demesne he heard a man's voice. It came out of a barred hut. As he turned toward it, he heard the voice cry, "A drink, a drink!"

"Who is within?" Colum-cille asked.

"Curnan, the son of the King of Connacht. A drink, a drink! I perish for lack of a drink!"

"Wert thou not, Curnan, under the security of the Clann Conaill?" Colum-cille said.

"The Clann Conaill is far away, and I perish here," Curnan said.

"You shall not perish," said Colum-cille. There were no guards at the hut; with a great stone he broke the bars. Then he saw Curnan: on the ground he lay, weak and emaciated, his eyes blinking in the light.

"I am Colum-cille of the Clann Conaill. Rise up and come with me."

"You are heaven-sent, Colum-cille. But can I go with you from Tara? I am a hostage from my father to King Dermott."

"I take you to your father. Come with me."

Thus Colum-cille did what the law forbade him to do—assist

the running away of a hostage. He and Curnan had to creep past the guards. They came to the tent that Colum-cille's attendants had set up outside the King's demesne.

"A drink, a drink!" implored Curnan when they came within the tent. Measure after measure of ale he drank, a supply sufficient for three harvesters. Nine loaves and six plates of meat were brought him, and he ate all at one sitting. But he could not lie down to take his rest, for now horns sounded: the search for the hostage had begun. Colum-cille and Curnan hurried away, facing toward Connacht, his attendants going another way. And as they went on with King Dermott's men pursuing them, the wrath in Colum-cille's breast grew more and more.

THE BATTLE

WEARIED and wayworn, Colum-cille and Curnan got into Connacht. Often they had to go into hiding on the way; they would have been waylaid at fords and passes were it not for warnings given them by wanderers who knew Colum-cille. From such folk he heard that King Dermott had sworn that he and the runaway hostage would not be let reach the King of Connacht's house alive —the guards he had sent after them had said this. His anger grew with the distance from Tara, and by the time they got into Connacht he had forgotten that he was a cleric and remembered only that he was the great-grandson of that over-sea raider, Niall, the King.

84

When they came to Curnan's father's house, they found the old King dead: he had been ailing, and the story brought to him of Curnan's treatment had broken the thread of his life. There was tumult and disturbance after the death of the King, and Colum-cille left Connacht, broken in body and with his spirit shattered.

Now as he went back to his own people he felt that for years and years of his life he had been borne up by some great winged creature—the eagle of his mother's dream. But now he was no longer borne up—he had fallen down upon the ground. He was on the ground since the judgment of King Dermott, since the time when he saw the hostility of those who stood to hear the judgment and knew from their looks that, in their minds, he was a dangerous self-seeker who sought to advance himself by bringing up these puzzling questions—he who had always been welcomed, who had always been admired. Until King Dermott acknowledged that his judgment had been wrong he could not feel as he used to feel— whole and upborne. The book would have to be delivered to him; he would have to show his possession of it.

And so when he went back to his kindred and found the chieftains of Clann Conaill all wrought up because King Dermott had sent fighting-men into Connacht, he did nothing to pacify them; rather, he spoke for war, saying to himself that battle would decide who should have possession of the book, and who was in the wrong and in the right in that assize of Tara.

He marched with the marching men. Clann Conaill joined forces with the men of Connacht and faced the fighting men of the

King of Ireland. And on the field that is named Cuil Dremne, King Dermott was defeated. Three thousand men were slain in that battle. And of the men who crossed the stream that divided the two armies, only one man returned: Colum-cille, standing by the pillar-stone of some ancient Pagan King, saw this lone fighter come back, and as he watched him triumphantly brandishing a blood-reddened spear, the sense of the slaughter made overcame him with horror and disgust, and he turned from the sight of the battle-field and went to where a river was flowing cleanly and peaceably.

A boat was on the river and he got into it and floated down. He floated on until he heard the sound of a bell ringing for vespers. He got out of the boat there and went to where a small church stood. An old man was ringing the bell as if he expected many to come to that forsaken place. Colum-cille was the only one. When he looked on the old man he knew him: he was Presbyter Fraech.

They sat together outside the little church and Colum-cille told Fraech about the battle he had been engaged in. And then he said, "It is not I who am to be blamed, but King Dermott on account of the wrong judgment that he gave against me."

"It were better that a cleric should submit to a wrong judgment than to set about defending himself by arms," said Fraech.

"When a man's wrath is stirred and he feels himself sore tried, it is hard for him to submit," said Colum-cille.

"It is right to stifle wrath lest it lead to slaughter," said Fraech.

"Though a man do ill through anger, yet God will pardon him if he do penance," said Colum-cille.

86

"It were better to shun evil than to seek forgiveness for having caused it," said Fraech.

"Nevertheless, we know," said Colum-cille, "that God and the host of Heaven have more joy for a sinner who returneth to them in repentance than for one who does no sin."

"Be it so," said Fraech, "and may God make us both good men together."

"Amen," said Colum-cille.

They sat there silently for some time, and then Colum-cille said, "Surely you will acknowledge, Fraech, that King Dermott gave a wrong judgment against me."

"Dermott judged according to his lights," said Fraech, "and they were very dim lights, friend Colum-cille. And as to the judgment, the generations that come will reverse it in your favor. But was there not heedlessness of others and much conceit in your own ways in your copying Finnen's book?"

"Then you would have it that Dermott was not in the wrong?" said Colum-cille after a while of silence.

"He gave a heedless judgment and you did a heedless act," said Fraech.

The next day Colum-cille journeyed back to his own cell in Derry. There was none of humankind there—only the creatures that he had made friends with: the crane that rested upon the roof of his hut, the cat that kept the mice away from the store of grain that he ground into meal, the wren that sang to him both inside and outside the hut, the fly that lighted on the page he might be reading and marked the line or the word he stopped at by remaining at the place. These pets were dear to Colum-cille, especially the three that remained with him in his hut.

One day when he was grinding meal at the quern, the wren suddenly flew down and caught the fly that was buzzing in the air. And the cat sprang up and caught the wren between her jaws. One would devour the other. There and then Colum-cille went down on his knees and prayed that God would prevent such destruction. Thereupon the cat let the wren flutter from between her jaws. And the wren opened its beak and let the fly go to rest upon Colum-cille's hand.

As he lay down to sleep that night, Colum-cille said to himself that men did as he had seen the cat and the wren do—the larger seizing the littler. And only a devotion that might reach to God could save men from doing this and so bringing about a state in which there would be neither law nor justice. And he knew that he himself had been destructive, seeing that three thousand men who might be alive that day were now dead through his urging of battle. Then he resolved that he would not stay two nights in the same place until he had gone to one of the chief saints of Ireland and had asked him to impose a penance upon him for what he had done.

THE EXILE

It was to Molaise, the saint whose abode was on Devenish, the island in Loch Erne, that Colum-cille went. He accused himself of having brought about a great slaughter, and he asked his confessor to lay a fitting penance upon him.

"The penance I lay upon you," said Molaise, "is a heavy one. It is that you leave your kindred and your country."

"For how long am I to bear this penance?" Colum-cille asked.

"Dear soul," said Molaise, "the penance that I lay upon you you will have to bear for the rest of your lifetime."

A great sadness came over Colum-cille on hearing these words. For a long time he was not able to move; he stood there like a crane that has forgotten how to make a flight. Then, when he spoke, it was to say a poem about the place where his cell and his church were:

> *Level your fields, and bright,*
> *Derry, where angels of God*
> *Are in the air around,*
> *Are upon every sod.*

He remembered his church that was called the Black Church, with the yew-tree growing before its door, and he said:

> *Dear to me is that yew—*
> *Would I were left in its stead!*
> *Pleasant the sight from my door,*
> *That tree with branches spread!*

89

Dear to him was Derry, and more and more dear it became to him after his return, as he waited there for his brethren to gather for their going with him, and for the ship to be built that would take him and them across the sea from Ireland. He took leave of the pets that had long been with him: the crane he permitted to go

back to the river-bank, the wren he let go back to its ivy-bush in the wood, and the fly went wherever the wind took it, while the cat went to Bauheen. The last wonder that was to be worked on his behalf while he was in Ireland had to do with this cat.

For Colum-cille kept a little cow to give milk to his cat—a cow that was named Blackie. Now while there was all the distraction of people coming and going about the place, the little cow was stolen. The cunning thief led her, a rope around her horns, along the dried bed of a river so that there would be no track of her hoofs upon the stones. The cat missed Blackie, and went mewing to this one and that one, asking them to find her. She led men down to the river-bed. And there, on the stones—a thing to wonder at —were the clear tracks of the cow's hoofs. The men followed the tracks down the river-bed and into a wood, the mewing cat going with them, and there, tied to a tree, was Blackie. Where she stood the marks of her hoofs stayed, and there a well burst up that is named Blackie's Well to this day. So Heaven deigned to have a wonder worked on his behalf before Colum-cille went from Ireland.

And now the ship was built and brought down to where Loch Foyle opens to the sea. Then Colum-cille left his cell and his church to others, and he blessed them who would be there after him, and he stepped into the small boat in which he would be rowed to the waiting ship. And he was no sooner in the boat than a huge fellow who was standing by, a forked club in his hands, pushed with all his might the boat away from the land. It was a graceless act, and all who were standing by thought so. And Colum-cille, between sadness and wrath, said to the fellow, "For the help you have given in getting me off from my land, I leave upon you the dole of exile, and upon every fellow who carries a forked club to this water-side, I leave the same dole."

The multitude along the sides of Lough Foyle stood silent, watching his boat being rowed out to the waiting ship. He went aboard and was welcomed by the brethren who were already there.

Then the sail was hoisted. No sooner was this done than a great cry of lamentation went up from the multitude upon the shores of Loch Foyle. And Colum-cille, hearing the cry that had so much sorrow in it, was greatly moved, and standing on the deck of the ship he said this poem:

Heart-troubling to me the cry
That comes on the wind;
The cry of Connal and Owen,
Kindred I leave behind.

Night falls, and from this
No night for me will go by
Without flow of my tears
For memory of this cry.

I care not that only a night
Be the length of life that is mine,
Since I leave them there, my own,
The tears in mine eyne.

There was among the brethren a monk named Odhran, an austere man, who went up to him and said, "Be silent! And if you cannot keep silence while listening to the lamentation from the shore, do not listen, but set your mind upon the holy work that we go to do in a strange land." "You are in the right, Odhran," said Colum-cille, but then he looked toward the people on the shore and saw their outstretched hands, and he said:

Oak-wooded Derry I leave,
And my heart is flooded with woe,
To think on the bleak fields,
And the outland folk I shall know.

Oak-woods to which I shall not
Ever come back home,
The faces of those I leave
Ever for this shall have gloom.

Too great the speed of my ship
From where all my love is due—
The beetle-browed Alban land—
Too swiftly it hurries to!

Then they were away from where they could see the throngs up the shores of Loch Foyle, and away from where they could hear their lamentations. Odhran said, "Now your hands need not stretch out toward their hands, nor your laments answer their laments." And as he said that, the sea gulls of Loch Foyle and the birds of the field and the wood flew around the ship in flocks and made a sorrowful crying. Colum-cille was so moved by the crying of the birds that he uttered this poem:

They will not come with me.
That cry along my wake—
Heavy it will be—
The parting we will make.

93

And when the birds of the field and the wood had ceased to fly after the ship, and while the sea gulls of Loch Foyle still flew after it, he said:

> I stretch my gaze across the main
> From lifting boards of oak—
> Many the tears in my gray eyes
> As backward I look.
>
> Gray eyes that always will look back
> To have Eire in their ken,
> Yet never will they rest upon
> Her women or her men.
>
> All woebegone am I who go
> Carried by wind and wave—
> "His-back-to-Ireland" is the name
> That I henceforth will have.

And having uttered this poem, Colum-cille said no other word of lamentation. Leaning upon Odhran's shoulder he gathered about him the brethren who were to labor with him in bringing the knowledge of Christ to the people of Alba and Britain who were still Pagan. There were with him twenty senior clergy, forty clergy, thirty deacons, and fifty young novices—a great and well-chosen company. They were bound for an island off the coast of Alba, a bleak island that was named Iona. There they could build a monastery, and till the fields, and instruct the youth who would come to them there, and send out missions to kings and princes on the mainland who were still Pagans. The sea they went across was dangerous and stormy, but without any loss or damage they came to that far island, Iona.

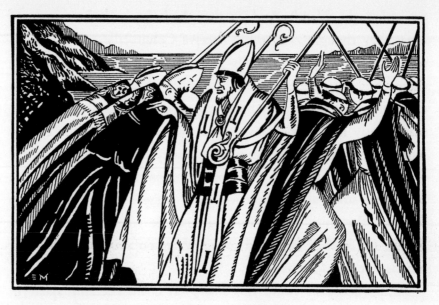

IONA AND THE DRUIDS THEREON

IT WAS on the Sunday of Pentecost that those on the ship sighted Iona. Colum-cille made up a chant on sight of the island, and the brethren repeated it as they sailed into the cove:

> *Iona, behold!*
> *Blessings on the eyes that see it!*
> *He who does a good for others*
> *Here, will find his own redoubled*
> *Many-fold!*

Now there were on the island a number of Druids who had the people subject to them because of the spells they uttered and the sorceries they performed. These false teachers were dismayed when they saw the company that carried the word of Christ approaching the island. And as they had deceived the people of Iona, they thought they could deceive Colum-cille and his brethren. Out of weeds and shells and bits of wreckage they made themselves what seemed to be the robes of monks and whatever else Colum-cille's company had on. And they stood above the cove, marvelously like to the company on the ship, so that the twenty senior clergy, the forty clergy, the thirty deacons and the fifty young novices thought they looked upon their fellows in the band that stood above the cove. And these deceivers shouted to those on the ship, "Why do you come to where there are men sowing the seed of faith and piety? Why do you not go to other islands, Orca or Colunsa?"

And when they heard this many on board the ship spoke in great concern, wondering why they had been directed to a place in which there were already men of faith and piety. But Colum-cille looking upon those above the cove knew them for deceivers: his eyes saw the falseness of their appearance: those who had mitres on their heads wore them awry, and their croziers were held downwards; there were spots of dirt on the robes that should be white and cleanly. He spoke to them from the ship, firmly denying their plea. And when they heard his words they could no longer keep the appearance they had put on: their robes became weeds, and what other things they had on became shells and bits of wreckage. Then all on the ship saw them for what they were—a band of naked Druids. Seeing they could not deceive the brethren the band hurried away to their own fastness.

Then the brethren landed, and Colum-cille blessed the island.

He and his monks began to build cells for themselves; they began the building of a church; they cleared and tilled the fields that were given them. Many folk of the island came to them for instruction and baptism, and later pious men of the Britons, Saxons and Picts joined their community.

There was on the island a very ancient man who had much authority among the folk, and he, though he was greatly enfeebled and lived at some distance away, decided to visit Colum-cille and the brethren. Hearing of this the Druids were very disturbed. For if this ancient man attached himself to the brethren, the rest of the folk of the island would forsake them. They resolved to go with the man to curse Colum-cille in his presence and the presence of his attendants: heretofore anyone they had cursed had fallen dead or had suffered some great affliction.

Pretending they were attendants of his they followed the litter on which the ancient man was carried to Colum-cille's cell. The litter was laid down, and Colum-cille came to him. But that ancient man could speak neither Irish nor Latin, and so they could say nothing that was intelligible to each other. The Druids made ready to curse Colum-cille. But as they did he raised his hand to bless the ancient man who had come to him. The Druids, stopped by that sign, could not speak. They turned around, and for the second time they went from before Colum-cille back to their fastness.

Then, through a man of tongues, that is to say, an interpreter, Colum-cille instructed the ancient man in the Faith, and his heart was moved, and he declared himself converted from Paganism, and he knelt down and asked that he be baptized into the faith in Christ. Colum-cille baptized him. And having received baptism, life went from the ancient man. Afterwards, where he was buried, his own people raised a great mound over him that is there to this day.

But a number of the folk of the island were still subject to the Druids. These false teachers had a well in which there was a dangerous power: if one drank of its water, or washed one's hands or feet in it, one was made deaf or blind, or stricken with paralysis. And the folk of the island honored this well, believing that the power of their ancient gods was in it, and the Druids were honored by them as the guardians of the well. And so they still kept a part of the people subject to them.

Colum-cille went to that well. And when the band of Druids saw him coming they rejoiced, for they would make him either drink out of the well or else acknowledge the potency of their god who dwelt in it. Colum-cille, not doubting the evil magic in the well, went to it. He knelt down and made the sign of the Cross over it, blessing it in the name of Our Lord. Then he drank the water, and washed his hands and feet in it. And he stood there to let the folk who crowded around see that he was not stricken by the power that was in the well. Thereupon, all knew that the spirit that had been in it had gone from it forever, and they were no longer in dread of the well, and they no longer feared the power of the Druids: And the well was not only harmless thereafter, but a source of healing: those who bathed in it or drank out of it were cured of deafness, or blindness, or paralysis. The Druids were left without any followers. This was the third time they had faced Colum-cille, and this time they did not go back to any fastness, but fled, like the swine that fled down a steep place, from Iona.

KING AEDAN

When all was settled on Iona—the fields cleared and the church built, the cells raised and the harvest stored—Colum-cille decided to visit a King on the mainland whose name was Aedan, and have him enter into agreements with other rulers to keep peace. Aedan ruled over a people in Alba whose tongue was the same as that of the people of Ireland: indeed he was of the same stock as Colum-cille. He had been baptized into the Faith, but he was a gross man and had no understanding of the sanctity of such a one as his visitor. And he thought he could justify his own ways if he could show that the cleric from Iona had the same wishes as he had. When it was told to him that Colum-cille was to visit him, Aedan prepared to make a mockery of him before the people. He had a young daughter who was very lovely: her he had arrayed in royal apparel, and he seated her in a chair opposite Colum-cille. And when he saw Colum-cille gazing earnestly at the maiden he was filled with glee; he thought that the other's pretended heedlessness of everything except the love of God would now be uncovered.

"Beautiful is the maiden," said he to Colum-cille.

"Beautiful indeed she is," said Colum-cille.

"Coinchenn is her name," said Aedan.

"Beautiful is that name," said Colum-cille.

"Thou dost desire to kiss Coinchenn," said Aedan.

"I do," said Colum-cille.

Aedan laughed saying, "Now my household will know what

manner of man you are, Colum-cille. As for myself, I am satisfied to let you kiss Coinchenn and take her in your arms."

Then said Colum-cille, "The maiden is beautiful in the sight of man, and I am one who has man's feelings. Nevertheless, these feelings can be so changed that they do not in any way come between one and the love of God. I honor the maiden, for I see in her the beauty that men see, and I see clearly a beauty that she has that is hidden from men." And saying this he went over to where the maiden sat, and he said to her:

> O unburdened soul,
> O unsullied mind,
> A kiss take from me—
> Give me kind!

He gave the maiden a kiss; she kissed him; they spoke not to each other, but the clearness of their faces was such that the King and his household were abashed. The maiden stood up from her chair and with bent head went from where they sat.

Then Aedan laid the disjointed blades of a shears before Colum-cille. He did this so that he might tempt him into a vain display of skill. But Colum-cille refused to put the blades together. "What have I to do with such wright's work? It would be only from vainglory that I should put the blades together."

And saying this he went out into a little wattled shed where he might kneel and pray as was his wont at vesper-time. The maiden who was watching for him followed, for she would look upon him when he was by himself and she was by herself. She half-opened the door to look where he was kneeling. She saw that his face had a light upon it and that there was an exceedingly bright light around his head. And so filled was she with wonder at what she saw that she did not move from where she stood. Then Colum-cille came out of the shed and saw her standing there. He gave her the broach that fastened his mantle and she gave him her broach.

And afterwards when the household saw how these two felt toward each other, they honored Colum-cille and they honored Coinchenn. Then Colum-cille and Aedan with all his family became firm friends, and Aedan did everything to protect Iona and to keep the amity among the rulers that Colum-cille desired.

In aftertimes when Colum-cille and Aedan were together, Aedan asked which of his younger sons should be King after him. Colum-cille told him that the one among them who should come to his arms without being so bidden should succeed to the kingdom of Alba. When the children came into the hall where the elders sat, one of them went straight to Colum-cille and gave him a kiss. He was Eochy; he was King after Aedan. Nevertheless, Eochy took part in a war which Colum-cille foresaw and warned many against taking part in: he was one of the outland allies of the King of Ulster, of Congal Claen, in his war against the King of Ireland, Donald. And in that war Congal Claen and his allies were defeated at the battle of Moyra.

As for Coinchenn, she treasured the broach that she had from

103

Colum-cille; she left it to her children, and her descendants held it as a most precious relic. She lamented greatly her brother going into the war that Colum-cille had forewarned all against.

That was long after Colum-cille, bringing Aedan over there, had crowned him in the church of Iona as King of all Alba. Iona, Alba, Ireland were all magnified on that day. When the crown had been placed on Aedan's head there were many who praised Colum-cille saying that there never was and never would be in Ireland or in Alba one who had so much of God's grace as he. Then Colum-cille, hearing such speech, came to them and reminded them of the vision that one of them, Bauheen, had had. "Tell it to us again, Bauheen," he said. "It seemed to me," said Bauheen, "that I looked into the Court of Heaven. I saw three chairs there; they were empty, and one was a chair of gold, and one a chair of silver, and one was a chair of crystal glass. I knew that they are for three who are now living in the world: the gold, the silver, and the crystal chair before the throne of the Lord."

"The golden chair that our brother saw was for Ciaran of Clonmacnoise, fitting the loftiness and strength of his piety," said Colum-cille. "The silver chair is for Molaise of Devenish, fitting the solidity and the brightness of his virtue; the third chair is mine own seat in the Court of Heaven. It is of crystal glass; it is the nature of crystal to be purely bright, letting this and that be seen through its substance. But it is fragile, and it is easy to check it with tints of all kinds." And Colum-cille looking on those who had come from Ireland to visit him repeated what he had once said to Bauheen. "I have such affection for my kinsmen that I am weak in favoring them. . . . And with the poets I am indulgent because of the delight I have in their art and because of my covetousness of their praises."

THIS is how Colum-cille lived in Iona in the days when he was growing to be an aged man: in the first part of the day he preached the word of God to all, bidding each one in the congregation love his neighbor as himself and to do this for the love of Our Lord. In the second part of the day he wove cloth for garments or he wrote, making copies of books. In the third part he worked with others tilling the monastery's fields. Then on certain days he went along the sea-shore, gathering dulse and shell-fish from the rocks, or he went out fishing, and this to help to provide for people who had no support. And in these days in Iona he often came face to face with the angel whom he had known for his guardian since his boyhood days.

It was long since he had seen that angel first. "God hath sent me to guard thee forever and always," he had said to Colum-cille. And when the boy, made afraid by his shining presence, had asked who he was, the radiant one had said, "Axal, I am called on earth, and for one to say 'Axal' is the same as to say 'Helper.' " And when young Colum-cille had asked if the angelic orders in the Court of Heaven were all of such brightness, Axal had said, "Though overwhelming it be to thee here, know that my brightness is seven times greater in the Court of Heaven." From that time Colum-cille had often known the presence of Axal.

Now when he had been a length of time in Iona Axal appeared to him again. In the night the angel stood beside where Colum-cille lay. In his hand he held a book of crystal. He motioned to put the book in Colum-cille's hand and have him open and read it. But Colum-cille would not take the book: he knew that what was written therein was a sentence which he had no wish to obey.

The angel went and the night passed. And on a second night the angel appeared with the crystal book and proffered it to him. But Colum-cille would not take it, and the angel went and the night passed. On a third night he came again and held the book to him. Colum-cille kept his hand away from it. Then the angel took a scourge from out of the folds of his garment and he struck Colum-cille on the side with it. The stroke the angel dealt did him much hurt, and in the morning he saw a welt left by that stroke—it was all down his right side.

Colum-cille repented that he was disobedient to Axal's will; he prayed that the angel might come to him again. And when on a fourth night the angel held the crystal book to him, he took it in his hand and opened it; he read the sentence that was therein. It was, "Prepare to return to thine own land and stay there for a while."

So he knew that he would have to go back to Ireland in spite of the vow he had made not to look on the face of a man or woman standing on Irish ground. And soon afterwards it was made known to him that the King of Ireland, Ae MacAinmire, had summoned a Council to meet at Drumceat and that issues affecting both countries were to be decided there. Envoys came to Iona from the people of Ireland telling him of their sorrow because of his absence and begging him to return and, for their sake, take part in the

Council. King Aedan, too, came to Iona to press him to come with him to Ireland.

Colum-cille, mindful of the sentence written in the crystal book, knew that he would have to go; it was his duty to take part in the Council. But he would not look on a man or woman on Irish ground. All the time he stayed there he would be unseeing; his cowl would be drawn down over his eyes. He took ship with King Aedan. They left the ship and went into a coracle when they came to an Irish port. And in the coracle they went up the little river that is named the Roa. So shallow is this water that no vessel had ever sailed on it before. But upon that low-watered river they went, sailing to the very place in which the Council was being held. And where they landed is called The Field of the Coracle to this day.

And when that tall figure with face half covered by a cowl stepped on the green, there was an outburst of welcome from all the gathering. Very seemly was all of him that might be seen. For although Colum-cille had imposed severe labors upon himself, and although his fasts and abstinences had been very great, he had not become strengthless nor uncomely: indeed, he had prayed to God that his appearance should not become unsightly. And God had heeded his prayer; he was always able to show a glad and handsome countenance to all.

The King of Ireland's son, Donald, he who was afterwards to win the battle of Moyra against the Ulster Prince who brought forces from Alba and Britain against him, came to meet Colum-cille and escort him to the pavilion where the kings and princes and high prelates held their session. The King of Ireland rose up and welcomed him and Aedan, and the welcome he gave to Colum-cille was not less than the welcome he gave to the King of Alba.

The great issue before the Council was one that affected Colum-cille as founder of Iona and as a former of the kingdom that Aedan ruled over. It concerned the territory that is called Dalriada; it lies across from Ireland, but it is one with the mainland of Alba. Now the King of Ireland maintained that he had a right to go into Dal-riada at any time and with any force that he might raise. King Aedan wanted to have this power abrogated. The difference be-tween the kings might lead to war between two kingdoms which spoke the same language and whose nobles were of the same de-scent (Aedan MacGovran himself was of Ireland) and which were linked together by the piety of Iona.

Aedan spoke in the Council, advocating that the King of Ire-land should forego his power of going into Dalriada. The men of Ireland murmured in opposition to this. Then a man who was learned in history and affairs spoke: Colman was his name. And Colman said that the King of Ireland should renounce his right of going into Dalriada, but that the men of Dalriada should pay him tribute, and that if the King of Alba went to the aid of the King of Ireland, the men of Dalriada should supply him with ships and give rations to his army.

Colum-cille then spoke in the Council. And so loving were the men of Ireland to him and so trustful of his judgment that they were ready to be ruled by what he said. And what he said was all in support of Colman's argument. Many spoke against Colman and Aedan and Colum-cille, but they were not able to remove from the main part of the Council the effect produced by the deep voice and the solemn words that came from the man with the cowl down over his eyes. At the end of the day the King of Ireland and his Councilors agreed to renounce the right of going into Dalriada and to accept the tribute and service that were offered. Then standing between Ae and Aedan, the King of Ireland and the King of Alba, and joining their hands together, Colum-cille said the words that were long remembered, "Let there be peace in perpetuity between the men of Eirin and the men of Alba."

There was brought to where the kings and princes and learned folk were assembled a skull that had been found where a road was being made below Tara. The skull was of such a size that no one then living bore a head that was nearly as large. All looked on that skull with awe. "It is a pity," said the King of Ireland to his Councilors, "that we cannot know what manner of man this great headpiece belonged to." Then Colum-cille prayed fervently that this might be revealed. Thereupon a voice that was heard by all related that this was the skull of that renowned King, Cormac MacAirt, son of Conn of the Hundred Battalions—the King who was ancestor to Colum-cille in the tenth generation. The voice was Cormac's own—he had permission, through the prayer of Colum-cille, to make himself heard there. And the voice related that while he had not been perfect of faith while he lived yet he had kept the truth as he knew it, and for that reason he was not among the lost. Colum-cille prayed devoutly to God on behalf of the soul of that well-deserving King; he washed the skull with his own hands and had it buried in sacred ground.

It was then that the Council came to deal with the case of the poets of Ireland. Colum-cille made plea that their order should not be abolished nor their guild dissolved, and that none of them should be banished out of Ireland.

"It is no easy thing to maintain them," said King Ae. "Their guild is too ungovernable; their demands upon rulers and people are exorbitant: you know very well, Colum-cille, that unless they are given large donations they make reviling and scoffing verses on people. I myself have suffered from their satire. This broach of mine, which is the handiwork of the greatest of artificers and which has been a treasured possession in my family for many generations, has been made the subject of a very mocking ballad. And," said Ae MacAinmire, " 'tis very little would start them deriding the crown that is upon my head." When he said this, the blind Dallan Forgail, the Chief-poet of Ireland, who was present, groaned aloud, turning his head this way and that way to find out if there was anyone in the Council who was favorable to the poets.

"The King's proposal is just and necessary," said Colum-cille's cousin, Bauheen, who had now become a tight-lipped prelate. "This ungovernable guild should be dissolved; there is no need for poets to belong to a privileged order, and certain of them should be banished as an example to others."

There were murmurs of approval for this and the blind Dallan Forgail groaned more loudly than before. He got up to address the Council, but he went into such long historical disquisitions that the Council lost all patience with him; some of them who had been favorable to the poets were made to think that King Ae's notion was a good one, and that it might be wise to start afresh.

Then Colum-cille, as one belonging to the guild of poets, stood up and spoke to the Council. He said, "A skull dug out of a hill is all that is Cormac MacAirt—a skull and a lettering upon a stone. But Cormac MacAirt, the noble, the generous, the beautiful, goes among us, making every one of us strive to be of his pattern. And what has made Cormac a pattern to men? Not his possessions, for they are long since gone. The praises the poets gave him are Cormac's lasting possession, and it is the poets who have given Cormac the life that he has for us. If there had been no poets to praise him that King like many another would now be only a skull and lettering upon a stone."

When Colum-cille said this, Bauheen answered him. "We have other things to think of besides fables, Colum-cille," he said.

Colum-cille answered, his voice rising to a chant:

> *If the poets' verse be fable,*
> *Then is all your knowledge fable.*
> *All your rights and state and power,*
> *And this drifting world is fable.*
>
> *For their fable which is lasting*
> *Give the fable that is passing!*
> *Kingly scarlet, scholars' blue*
> *Will make no show in hereafter.*

God has dowered sons of Adam
With a craft for them to work on;
Honor then the craft that's proven,
Give the craftsman means to live by.

When Colum-cille had spoken in this wise the mind of the Council was no longer hardened against the poets. Then it was agreed that whatever judgment Colum-cille gave the Council and the Guild of Poets would abide by. Colum-cille gave this judgment:

That each district should maintain a principal poet and his students who would celebrate the deeds of the clans of that district and keep the memory of their forefathers fresh and stirring.

That the principal poet of one district should not go into another district for goods or preferment without leave of his lord; that if he made a poem that was of interest to the people of another district the lord of that district would send his principal poet to meet him at the border and have him recite the poem. And if he judged it worthy, that other poet was to reward him who made it and bring it back to his lord. And if this other poet did not find it worthy the one who made it was to go back without any reward.

That the poets were no longer to go about in bands, quartering themselves for long seasons on this or that ruler; that none of them should be banished; that their privileged order should be kept in existence, and that their guild should not be dissolved.

The Council accepted this judgment and the poets were content with it. Their franchise was curtailed, but they had still their guild; their order remained a privileged one, and, happily, none of them were banished out of Ireland.

The next day the head professor of every grade of the Bardic Assembly came and recited a poem of eulogy of Colum-cille. Standing before him, one and then the other of them recited his praise. And when he heard the praises of himself chanted by the poets of Ireland, the heart within Colum-cille swelled and his mind became lit up, and such was his exultation that the air above his head became filled with evil spirits who gloated over his loss of humility and his access of vainglory. Bauheen, the thin-lipped one, who was beside him, perceived this; he rebuked him sharply, telling him that it was not right that he should take such account of the world's praises and that he should consider only his duty to God. And when he heard that rebuke and knew its justice, Colum-cille covered his head with his mantle and wept sorely, repenting of the vanity that he had given way to. As he wept the evil spirits who were above his head dispersed, leaving the air clear. Then Colum-cille spoke to the poets and told them that they were not to write down the praises of him that they had made, and that they were not to make them known to men.

"But," said Bauheen to him afterwards, "it is known that the Chief-poet of Ireland, Dallan Forgail, is making a eulogy of you. You have done nothing to withhold him from doing this."

"Service for service—it is that that keeps a folk together, cousin Bauheen," said Colum-cille cheerfully. "It is right that the Chief-poet of Ireland should make a eulogy of me on account of the benefit I have done his order."

"But then," said Bauheen, "everybody will be reciting Dallan's poem and Alba and Ireland will be filled with your praise. How will you be able to keep your humility with such urgings to vainglory?"

Colum-cille smiled on his cousin. "Dallan is a very skilled poet," he said, "and I have asked him to use all his art in making this commemorative poem. And I promise you, Bauheen, that not more plentiful than hornless piebald cows are the men in Ireland and Alba that will be able to remember the poem that Dallan uses all his skill in the making of."

And so it came to be. Dallan Forgail's poem was praised by every poet in Eirin because of the strangeness of its rhythm and the depth and density of its references. "Amra," which means strange, is the title that that poem of Dallan's is known by. We have been told that the clerk of water in Armagh got the first part of the poem by heart, and he was so bent on knowing the second part that he made a pilgrimage to the tomb of Colum-cille, and prayed and fasted there to the end that his mind would be so illuminated that he would be able to memorize the second part. In the morning he was able to repeat the second part and he jumped about with joy. But when he tried to repeat the first part he found that he could not bring the lines of it together. Fast and pray as he might he was never able to get into his mind any but the first or the second part: never the whole of the "Amra" did that man know. Still, if the clerk had not been a drunken fellow, we have no doubt but by grace of Colum-cille, his patron, he would have been able to get by heart the whole of Dallan Forgail's eulogy.

THE VOYAGE OF THE SONS OF KING LEWY

WHEN he returned from Drumceat a matter was brought for judgment before King Ae in his court at Tara.

It concerned two sons of a provincial King: by mischance one of them had killed a third brother; the question brought up for judgment was what inheritance each should have from his father and from the brother who had been slain. And the judgment given at Tara was not accepted by either of them.

Then it looked as if the dispute would drag on until the old King, their father, came to die, and would then be ended by some violent action. "But there is still a peacemaker in the Western World," their father said to himself, and he asked his sons to go across the sea to Iona, submit their case to Colum-cille, and abide by the judgment he would make. The two—their names were Cairbri and Crimhaun—agreed to do this.

They had gone hunting with a third brother whose name was

Cael. And in making a cast of a spear at a stag Cairbri had pierced him, killing Cael there and then. Great had been the disturbance after this untoward happening. Cael had been named as his father's successor, and now it could not be decided whether the succession should go to Cairbri or to Crimhaun. Also there was the question of Cael's possessions: was Cairbri entitled to a share of them or should they go wholly to Crimhaun? These questions could not be decided at home and they could not be decided at Tara. And his domain was filled with disputes and distractions until that provincial King—Lewy Red-hand was his name—bade his sons go over to Colum-cille, ordering a ship to be made ready for their sailing from Derry in the early springtime.

And so with their two wives and their wives' two waiting-women, with four and twenty warriors, and with gillies to hunt and fish for them and to dress and cook the provisions they brought with them, Cairbri and Crimhaun journeyed toward where the ship was being made ready for them. In a forest of the north they came upon a hermit; they liked his discourse so well that they listened day after day to him. This hermit was none other than Mongan, that Prince of Faerie whom Colum-cille had converted to the Christian Faith.

There were times when Mongan remembered his former state and when a desire to visit the Hidden Islands he had known would come over him. That longing was on him now. And a ship that he could voyage in was being made ready for the sons of King Lewy. But he had made a vow not to leave his cell until spring-

time. And so Mongan chanted this poem to the two princes who
stood outside his cell in the forest.

O sons of King Lewy,
Have patience and tarry
Till a time that is fitting
For sailing has come!

The North Wind blows harshly,
The waves are unbridled,
The thick mists are hiding
The coasts from one's eyes!

The season that's fitting
For sailing is Summer,
When birds sport in invers
And salmon leap waves.

The more ships are sailing
The more each has safeness—
O sons of King Lewy,
Remain here a while;

Here make your encampment,
And tusked boar and badger
Give chase to till season
For sailing has come!

The two sons of Lewy Red-hand with their wives and their following built bothies there and stayed in the forest near where Mongan had his cell. They hunted and lived on the provision the gillies had brought. And so the spring passed and summer came. Then they made their way toward where their ship stayed in readiness for them.

Mongan went before them. He was there when they came to the ship-stead; he had put on the appearance of the master of the ship whom he had sent into the forest to meet the voyagers. And the two sons of King Lewy went on board the ship that had Mongan for its master, and with them went their wives and their wives' waiting-women, and their warriors, and the gillies who would fish while they were on the sea and who carried nets and lines with them.

As soon as the ship was outside Loch Foyle a blast of wind came up and blew it in another direction from Iona. For days and nights they were driven by that blast. A great thirst assailed the sons of Lewy and their company. They were dried up within and without by that thirst. But then a morning came when they heard the sound of the waves breaking upon a shore. Mists went, and they saw an island over which bent a rainbow that had marvelous depth in its seven colors. They went on land, and they saw wells and streams and pools and steep water-falls—it was an island of waters. They drank with their mouths to the wells and they steeped their bodies in the pools. Then for a whole day they went along and across the island, but they saw no man nor woman on it, no bird nor beast. In the middle was a pool; deep it was and deep blue was its water. A man was standing by it: at first they thought that he was the last of the island's dwellers, but then they saw that he was their shipmaster. "Our race shrinks," he said. "Once there were many here."

They went back on their ship and a wind carried them away from that island. They slept, and when they awakened they heard waves breaking on a shore. Their ship had come to an island that was deeply wooded. They went along paths over which branches grew; honey and gums dropped from the branches. And they saw no man nor woman, no bird nor beast where they went. But folk had been on the island once; many signs made them know that. There was a lake in the middle of the island, and in the midst of its clear water was an islet: there was a bower on it that was made of that shining substance of the sea that is called margaret. No one was in its beautiful chamber. The light that came through its walls fell on him who was the shipmaster and made him look as if he could never be care-worn nor decrepit. But unsmiling he was when he went from that place with them. "Many and proud were they who were here," he said, "and none is left now to give us a welcome."

Then they set their ship on the ridge of the sea and for three days and three nights they sailed on. They came to another island. Landing on it they saw a house on a height: there were two hundred doors to that house, and as the voyagers approached they were all flung open in welcome for them. Very few were the folk in that wide and high house. But they were a happy-looking company, and they served all who had come from the ship with rich-tasting food and well-brewed ale. The voyagers and they made merry all the night; in the morning the two companies went down to the ship holding each other by the hands. Those on the island would have made the ship-master King over them, but crying out that all was changed for him, he went upon the ship, and they sailed away.

They came to another island: it was all one wide green plain; in the middle of it a high, many-branched tree was growing. All had room beneath the branches of that great tree. And as they stayed there a flock of birds flew to the branches. They sang from every branch. From morning till noon they sang of the happenings in the world to the time when Our Lord was born. And from noon till midday they sang of His birth and of all that He did while on earth. Then from midday till night they sang of the Day of Judgment and of the solemn things that would be brought to pass on that day. And as they sang the birds clapped their wings and struck their beaks into their sides so that drops of blood like rain fell down upon those who, entranced, stood under that tree. And the tidings that these silver-winged birds sang became too solemn for these men and women to bear. They went away with their heads muffled in their mantles. And one of the birds flying after them dropped a leaf of the tree before one of King Lewy's sons, a golden leaf. He took it up; they all went on their ship.

A blast of wind came up and drove the ship along. For many days and nights they went swiftly on, seeing no land. Then the wind ceased to blow on them, and when they were able to look about them they saw that they were outside Loch Foyle. The wind that came then bore them toward Iona. Over the long green waves, over the deep-sounding waves they went and came in good time to the island where Colum-cille and his companions abode.

Colum-cille was walking in the churchyard when the ship came into port. He knew that sons of a king of Ireland were on that ship, and he said to those who were with him:

> 'Tis time for fire in the guest-house,
> And welcome with open hand;
> We will cheer them and they will cheer us
> With tidings from our own land.

He went to the port and greeted the sons of Lewy Red-hand and their wives and all their followers. And the next day he gave judgment in the case that they submitted to him. To Cairbri he awarded the succession although it was Cairbri who had done the slaying, for he knew that Cairbri was righteous and brave, and to Crimhaun he awarded all Cael's possessions. The two sons of King Lewy accepted this judgment, and they went back and kept peace in their father's realm. Cairbri who had carried it left the golden leaf as an offering on the altar of Colum-cille's church.

Colum-cille knew who their ship-master was. He embraced Mongan and asked him gently why he had left his cell in the forest. And Mongan confessed to him that, as he had been one who went much upon the sea, an island rather than a forest-glade would be the place for him to live in solitariness. Colum-cille smiled on him and brought him to an islet where he could build his cell.

And later he permitted Mongan to serve the brethren of Iona. For it happened that certain outlaws living on a barren headland had taken to slaughtering the seals that brought up their young on rocks near Iona. He had asked these men to desist from the slaughter of the seals. But they had told him that unless they had seal-meat they would starve, for they had no sheep, nor cattle, nor pigs. Colum-cille to save the seals agreed to send the outlaws meat from Iona. Mongan took upon himself the duty of bringing the meat to the outlaws every Monday. And other days he went to the rocks to see that they kept their pledge and did not disturb the seals. And he would cheer Colum-cille by telling him how the seal-families increased and how more and more of them were to be seen on the rocks. And so Mongan served the brethren on Iona for many seasons.

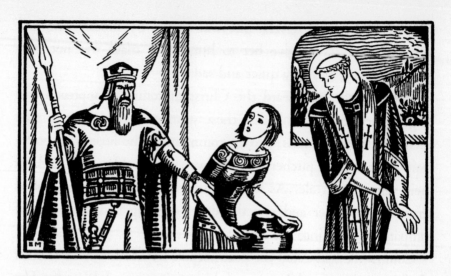

AFTER THE COUNCIL

THERE was one more King on the mainland whom Colum-cille had not won over to amity with the other rulers nor to friendliness to Iona. This was Bruidhe of Pictland. Bruidhe was unconverted, and indeed had a great enmity to the Christian Faith. He had this enmity mainly because of his Councilor whose name was Brocan: he was a Druid. Now when Brocan learned of the coming of Colum-cille and his company to Pictland he counseled the Pagan King not to receive him, but rather to put locks of iron on his doors so that the Christian company might not enter his royal dwelling. Bruidhe did according to his Druid's counsel. He and his household were told of the approach of the company from Iona; they did not go to welcome them, but sat in the hall drinking ale out of vessels of glass. And while they sat there they were served by a little maid: she was the daughter of Irish people, and had been carried off from near Derry by reivers. She was owned by Brocan who had forced the reivers to give her to him. This maid was not full-grown yet, and was very quiet and sad.

Those in the hall heard the Christian company approach and laughed heartily to think that these strangers would have to stay outside with the hounds. Brocan commanded the little Irish bond-maid to carry in a pitcher that she was hardly able to lift and fill their vessels with ale. As she did this for the King, she looked across her shoulder and saw the doors opening and a white-clad company coming into the hall.

Colum-cille had asked the door-keepers for admission on account of the weariness and hunger of his company and himself. The door-keepers had told him that they had no way of opening the doors. Then Colum-cille had made the sign of the Cross over the locks and they had fallen off the doors. So he and his company came into King Bruidhe's hall.

Greatly astonished was the King at this power to come into the place in spite of locks of iron. And with astonishment went respect for Colum-cille and the message that he bore. He caused him to sit beside him. But Brocan was made angry and sullen by Colum-cille's power and the sign of the King's favor. Still he thought that Colum-cille had nothing more than magic—the sort of magic that he himself had—and that in time he would have a chance of using a stronger magic against him and so humbling Colum-cille.

Bruidhe and Colum-cille discoursed on things of high import—of the making of amity between the Kings of Ireland and Alba and Britain, and of an agreement between them all to make Iona free from raids and attacks and of the taking of disputes to a council at Iona. But the more earnestly they talked the more glowering Brocan became. And when Colum-cille spoke pleasantly to the little bond-maid, Brocan shouted at him, "She is mine, and is not to be spoken to without my leave." The little bond-maid wept, thinking on the fearful things that might be done to her afterwards.

Colum-cille, knowing by her speech that she was from near his own dear Derry, took her hand and said, "No evil thing will befall you, daughter, and with God's help you shall be brought back to your own land and your own relations." When he heard this said, Brocan sprang up and pulled the bond-maid over to him, holding her arm.

Then Colum-cille said, "Know, O Brocan, that unless you free this captive your life will leave you in a short space."

"I shall not free her," Brocan said. "She is mine."

"Ere the night is passed," said Colum-cille, "the vessel of glass that you drink out of will break in your hand without anything touching it, and that will be a sign to you that your death will follow. Assuredly it will follow unless you permit this captive to go with those who will take her back to her own land and her own relations."

Then Brocan swore by his deities—those deaf and dumb gods of Druidism—that he would not let his bond-maid go. Soon Colum-cille took his leave of the King and his household, thanking them all graciously for the reception they had given him and his company. They went out of the hall, and the bond-maid sighed to see them go.

They journeyed on and came to a little river that is named the Nesa. And when Colum-cille was crossing and in the middle of the river, he stooped down and took a stone up from its bed. Then he stood in silence on the bank, holding the stone in his hand, and his companions wondered what was passing through his mind.

As they stayed, a messenger came up on horseback. He was of Bruidhe's household and had followed them swiftly. For as Brocan was drinking his ale the glass vessel in his hand broke without anything being near it; he was affrighted and declared that he would let the bond-maid go if Colum-cille would avert from him the doom of death.

Then Colum-cille put the stone out of the river-bed in the hand of the messenger and bade him tell Brocan to put it in the vessel he drank from. Then the qualms and shakes would pass from him. But he would have to drink with the intention of sending the bond-maid to where they would be waiting—here, by the bank of the Nesa. The messenger hurried back to the King's hall. He gave the stone to the King's Druid. When Brocan put it in the vessel and drank, the qualms and shakings went from him. He pushed the little bond-maid from him, and the messenger took her on the horse before him and rode to where Colum-cille and his company waited.

Colum-cille received the little maid and put her in charge of two of the brethren, requiring them to take her across the sea to Ireland and put her into the hands of her relations. Then, with the little maid in their company, they all went to where there was a ship to carry them away from King Bruidhe's dominion.

But now that the qualms and shakings had gone from him, Bro-can repented him that he had let his captive go. He mounted his chariot and hurried to the stead from which Colum-cille's ship would sail. And there he came upon the company with the little maid in their midst. He demanded of Colum-cille that he give him back his bond-maid. But she clung to Colum-cille and he would not let her be taken away. Then the Druid declared that he would raise a storm and mist that would prevent their ship's sailing. And by the magical powers that he had he caused a thick mist to appear and winds to rise and blow against them. The master of the ship begged Colum-cille not to go on board and to make peace with the Druid by giving his bond-maid back to him. But Colum-cille said, "The powers of the true God are high above all sorceries. Trusting in them we will go on the ship and sail the sea." So he went aboard, he and his company with the little maid. He made the crew hoist the sails, setting toward the mist and the storm. And as they sailed on the magic wind became stilled and the magic mist lifted, and there was a fair breeze for them and a clear way. For what the Druid had raised were only appearances to deceive those who could be got to believe in them.

The sailing forth of Colum-cille led to the conversion of King Bruidhe. Seeing that he was not able to prevail against the apostle of the new faith, the King no longer put trust in him and ban-ished the Druid from his side. And he turned more and more to Co-lum-cille and to the brethren in Iona and took counsel from them. And as for the little Irish maid, she was brought back to her own country and to the house of her father's brother.

THE LAST DAYS IN IONA

IN DAYS after this Colum-cille would often speak of that little maid who was now rearing her children near places he had known, and he would guess at what field her husband tilled or the hill-slope that she took her cows or sheep to graze on. They were near Derry, these fields, and of all the places he had known Derry was the one that was closest to his heart. At this time he made a poem about places that he had lived in and loved, and the place that he spoke about with most love was Derry. He was glad when a youth came to join his community from Derry; this novice was kin to her who had been Brocan's bond-maid.

He called him to him one day from where he was working in the field. It was a Saturday, and Colum-cille had finished reading his office. "Beloved son," he said to the novice, "I charge you, after the hour of nones on Monday, to go to the look-out and watch for a noble guest whom I am expecting. Through the air that guest will come, for she is a crane. She is coming from my own place in Ireland and will sojourn with us for a while. But she will be very spent and weary; her strength will be failing as she arrives, by reason of the length of her journey. She will not be able to go farther than where the wave and strand meet, for the wave will drive her back and she will not have strength enough to make the shore. Do thou, beloved son, be ready to aid her." And Colum-cille told the novice, "Bring her into the kitchen and give her food; for three days and three nights we will have to care for her. Then she will leave us and go back to Ireland. I am putting this task on thee rather than on another because thou and the crane and myself are of the one neighborhood, and thou art bound to have compassion upon her and show her kindness and serve her better than might any of the others."

The day passed and the next day, and the novice went to the look-out after nones on Monday. He was no sooner there than he espied a crane winging wearily toward the shore. When she came down she was not able to make her way through the roughness of the sea. He went to her and lifted her up and carried her into the kitchen of the monastery. Colum-cille was there, and he said to the novice, "May God bless thee for the service thou hast done for her who has made a pilgrimage to us." The novice laid her down beside him, and the crane nestled close to him and ate from his hand; she would not be put from him as long as she was in Iona. At the end of the third day she fluttered before him, and, flapping her wings, uttered cries. Colum-cille said to the brethren, "She would take leave of us and return to her own land. And well may she be sorrowful on leaving me," said Colum-cille, "for I shall be sad at heart for this leave-taking."

The crane made her farewell to him and to the brethren, and he blessed her. She rose up and turned toward Ireland. As they watched her wing her way, Colum-cille repeated the poem he had made:

> *Places my memory holds—*
> *Durrow, Assaroe;*
> *Drumcliff with acorns filled,*
> *Drumhome with growth of sloe!*

132

The dark sea reddened at set
Of sun, where the sea gulls soar;
Then, fair and inviting, the slope
Of Derry—my heart goes before

To watch across Loch Foyle
What time the swans are there,
Single upon the wave,
Or winging, pair and pair!

If I owned Alba, all
The land and the sea around,
I would give it for the width
Of a cell on Derry's ground!

It was now four and thirty years since he had left Ireland. His voice which could have been heard at the great distance of fifteen hundred paces could now only carry to the door of his church, and he who used to stride from end to end of the island had now to go in a chariot from place to place. A day came when he went in his chariot; leaving it with the driver he made his way to the top of a hillock that overlooks the level lands. It was in that bright and hopeful season that is between the feast of Our Lord's resurrection and the coming of the Holy Ghost, and what he looked on was fair and prosperous. He saw the church he had built and the reed-thatched cells of his monks surrounding the monastic building; he saw the cultivated fields with the grain standing high in them, and he saw the grazing-fields with their fresh grass. All this had been made out of wildness and barbarism in half the years that are given man to live on the earth.

And Colum-cille thought that though small and unnoted was that church built of hewn oak with its roof thatched with reeds, yet the kings and people of Alba would come to do worship in it, and not only they but the kings and people of other parts of the Western World. "Peace, Fellowship—these are Iona," he said to himself.

As he stood upon that hillock leaning on his staff, he perceived three who stood a little away from him as if going from that hillock. They were three maidens. "Who and whence are ye?" Colum-cille asked them in great astonishment. "We are Vision, Achievement and Prophecy," they said, "and we have been long with you, Colum-cille." They moved toward the edge of the hillock, and Colum-cille cried to them, "Do you go from me now, Vision, Achievement and Prophecy?" They answered, saying, "We go from you now." "Will what I have done remain?" he asked them. Then she who was named Prophecy turned to him and said, "What has been done here will remain for many ages, and Iona will be a place toward which shall turn for peace and order the Scots of Eirin and Alba, the Picts, the Britons and the Saxons—all the folk of these islands which are a world to themselves." "And my own life?" asked Colum-cille. "Thou hast reached the end of it," the maiden said. The three were gone from the hillock even as she spoke.

The end of his life was near and all this would have to be left behind—all this that he had built and blessed and cultivated in the midst of the rough sea. Men whom he could not know would preach in the church, and direct the brethren, and have books copied for other monasteries, and bring about the fellowship of the people through their kings. And he would have to resign it all to them.

A great sadness such as might come upon one who had lost his last battle and had no aid nor refuge before him came over Colum-cille. He laid himself down on the hillock, his face on the ground. "If God had truly loved me," he complained, "it would have been granted to me to come on death suddenly so that I should not know what I had to go from—it is the going from the work of one's life that makes the hardship of death."

Long he stayed there, stretched upon the ground. Then very sadly he rose up and went to where his chariot was, and he drove along the sea-shore. Now when he came to the port he saw that a very strange thing had befallen. A ship that had curious figures carved upon it had come to Iona. Seven persons landed from it, six youths and a maiden. Their figures were wasted, but all who looked upon them saw nobility in their dark faces and beauty in their great dark eyes. Speaking brokenly in the Latin tongue they declared themselves to be the seven children of the King of India. From the farthest of all lands they had made a journey to Iona that they might be in fellowship with Colum-cille: hearing about him they had come to love him. For many months they had sailed the seas.

With great love Colum-cille took them into his fellowship; for a month they were with him night and day. But the fatigues they had undergone were so grievous and heavy that they wasted away and died, each of them on the bosom of Colum-cille, and they praised God for having seen him and conversed with him. They died, these seven children of the King of India, in faith in God and in surety of the Resurrection, and they were buried in Iona. Their graves are known as the Graves of the Seven to this day.

During the time they were with him the sadness that had come upon Colum-cille on the hillock lessened day by day. When they were laid to rest the sadness went altogether from him. He stood up and crossed himself in the Name of the Father, Son, and Holy Ghost. He spoke, and his voice in that place sounded with as much resonance as ever it had, "I go and leave all that has been done in His hands."

Thereupon he went into the barnyard of the monastery. And Dermott who was there spoke to him about the good harvest that was in prospect and showed him the bins of grain that were still left them. Colum-cille blessed the bins and said that since the time had come for him to leave them he was well contented in knowing that they would have sufficiency for the year. Dermott, deeming that he, their father, was thinking of a visit to the mainland, went on counting the stores in the yard and the barn. He came upon a jar filled with nuts; showing them he said to Colum-cille, "Father, it was told to me that in far-back days a priest whose name was Mochta was here, and that his gillie brought a cap-full of nuts to him. But Mochta would not take them. "Not to me belongs the fruit of Iona," he said, "and let it be ungathered until its proper owner comes." "When will that proper owner come?" his gillie asked him. "Long hence," said Mochta, "and his name shall be Colum-cille." Colum-cille smiled and said cheerfully, "we are beholden to Mochta for leaving the fruit of Iona for us. But we are going to leave to others much more than the nuts of the glades—we are going to leave the fruit, not of the ground, but of our spirit."

Then he left the barnyard to return to the monastery; and Dermott, busying himself with this and that saw he went unattended and that his gait was feeble. It was but a little way from the barnyard to the monastery, but Colum-cille was forced to rest himself before he went half the way. And while he was there, seated on a broken wall, the horse that used to carry the milk-vessels for the monastery—an old white horse he was—came to him. And the horse laid his head upon Colum-cille's shoulder and wept against his cheek. Great tears fell from the eyes of the old horse; he wept as if he were bidding farewell to a well-loved comrade whom he had no hope of ever seeing again. Dermott, hurrying out of the yard, came to where the pair were. And seeing the horse resting his head upon the father's shoulder he would have driven him away. Colum-cille would not have him do this. And he said that God had willed that the dumb beast should have knowledge of his approaching death while none of the brethren had such knowledge. The old horse turned and went stumbling to his lair, and Colum-cille, attended by Dermott, went into the monastery.

It was the hour at which he was wont to write, copying the scriptures so there might be no lack of holy books in the monasteries of the west. He went into the writing-hall and went on with what he had been writing. And he wrote down to the thirtieth psalm and to the line *Inquirentes autem Dominum non deficent omni bono,* or, as we should say, "There shall be no lack of good things

137

to those that seek the Lord from the heart." Having written this line he said that it was time for him to leave off writing. He left the next verse to be written by another—*Venite filii, audite me, timorem Domini docebo vos,* or, as we should say, "Come, beloved children, and harken to me, and I will instruct you in the fear of the Lord." Leaving the writing-hall he went into his cell and lay down upon his couch.

When at midnight the sacristan struck the bell, he rose up and went into the church alone. He went on his knees before the high altar and prayed with fervent heart, saying nothing in words. Dermott, coming within, found the church filled with light. But as he went toward the altar the light was no more, and he had to grope with his hands to find Colum-cille. Finding him he sat beside him holding his head on his bosom. They had not stayed like this long before the rest of the brethren entered, lighted candles in their hands. Perceiving how faint he was they made lament around him. He signed to Dermott to raise his hand (he himself was not now able to raise it), and Dermott raised the hand of Colum-cille and the dying man without speaking gave all who were there his blessing. As he did this the spirit departed from him.

Then the brethren bore the body into the refectory and laid it out there. In the place of refreshment and meeting they had been cheerful in spite of the long vigils and great hardships that were their lives; they had been even glad and merry because of the good fellowship which their father, Colum-cille, had shed around. Now they were downcast and in great sorrow, thinking that never again would they hear that voice speaking to them and speaking for

them, and never again would they see him striding from the monastery to the fields, or working there, his back bent with the others, and never again would they see him in the writing-hall, his hand moving swiftly across the page. As they knelt around where they had laid him they heard a great storm come up and they heard the sea rising and lashing against the shore of the island.

But that was well, they said to one another. For they remembered that he had said that when he came to die he would prefer to be buried by his brethren in quietness and peace, without crowds making a turmoil about his resting-place. The storm would last, they said to one another, until their father was buried, and no one would be able to come to them from the mainland.

And so it was. For the three days and three nights that his body was waked, storm and tempest were around Iona, and no one was able to come to it from the mainland. With only the brethren around it Colum-cille was laid in his grave. Thereafter the storm abated and the sun came out; it shone on a calm sea, and on the grain-fields and the pasture-fields and the apple-yards and all looked bright and promising. Colum-cille was born in December and he died in June. Severe was his life in respect to labors and austerities, and it was fitting that he should enter it in the winter month. But pure and bright was the soul that he bore through the world, and it was fitting that his time for leaving it should have been the brightest and most shining season of the year. Before his time there were saints in Ireland who might be compared with mills that, by the water of the grace of God, ground the grain that Saint Patrick had sown. But in their cases, weed and dust mingled with the grain because of the hard-heartedness of our forefathers who sowed tares among the crop it was theirs to gather. But the grain that Colum-cille ground was the pure white flour of the Word of God.

"IT IS unchanged," one man said to another as the two stood in Glen Colum-cille in Tir-connal. "It must have been like this when Colum-cille played here, when nearly the whole of Northern Europe was Pagan still. A dark glen except for the mountain-ash with its bunches of scarlet berries and the foxglove with its purple bells growing against the stones!" He who spoke was the younger of the two: his dress showed that he was from the country that had once been Dalriada and Alba and Pictoria and had grown to be Scotland: he wore kilts, a cap with a feather in it, and a mantle fastened with a broach. The man he spoke to, an older man, belonged to Tir-connal, and wore the clothes of gray stuff that had been woven in a house near by. They spoke in Gaelic to each other.

"What is your name?" the elder asked.

"Malcolm MacCuilim."

"The saint's name doubled: Malcolm—Maoil-Chuilim—Dedicated to Saint Columba."

"It was the royal name in Scotland after Columba's time."

"And mine is that of the Prince of Tir-connal who wrote the Life of Columba when Henry the Eighth was King of England—Manus O'Donnell."

"You are a shanachie, Manus?"

"I am—the story-teller and historian of the parish."

Malcolm laughed. "Since I have come on this pilgrimage," he

said, "I have found out that the shanachies of Ireland will not own that the body of Colum-cille rests in our side of the world—in Iona. You will have to tell me why they say so."

Manus O'Donnell did not smile though there was something very whimsical in the gravity he assumed and the way he shook his head. "My young hero," he said, "what the shanachies of Ireland say is very well-corroborated history. I will tell it to you before the pilgrims come into the glen."

He sat on a stone and the young man in the kilts stood before him, his arms folded, a man evidently used to listening to narrations. Manus O'Donnell said:

"Toward the end of his long mission Saint Patrick began to wonder how the faith he had labored to bring them would be kept in the after-times by the men and women of Ireland. He prayed that he might have knowledge of how it would be. Then his angel appeared to him and said, 'In your sleep to-night a vision will be shown you and from it you shall know how faith and devotion will be in Ireland after you have gone to your reward.' Saint Patrick slept, and in his sleep he saw the plains and mountains of Ireland all in a blaze. Flames mounted to the sky in the east and the west, the south and the north. Then they sank down, and only on ridges that were distant from each other were there flames. And these separated flames sank until they were only like lamps or candles that the wind might blow out. Then they could only be seen as sparks and feeble glows that were no more than the kindlings of fires.

"While he wondered what this vision might mean his angel came before him and said that as the high and unseparated flames had sunken into glows that were distant from each other, so the faith he had labored to arouse in Ireland would, after his time, sink down and would be only glows, and those among people far separated from each other. Saint Patrick wept when this was told him. His angel said to him after a while: 'Look to the north and you will see a change wrought by the right hand of God.' Saint Patrick looked, and behold! a flame rose in the north, not great in the beginning, but ever-growing until it caught up the separated glows and filled the darkness. Ireland and beyond Ireland was lighted by that flame. But it, too, died down, and again there were only sparks and glows on certain heights. These were not as feeble as before.

"The flame in the north, the angel said, represented one who would appear there. Colum-cille would be his name. He it would be who would raise the flame again and spread it beyond the shores of Ireland. And the blaze that Saint Patrick had kindled would never after Colum-cille's time become as feeble as it had been before. Saint Patrick was comforted by this and he said to the angel, 'May it be that this Colum-cille have a place in the same grave as myself and Saint Brigid.'

"After this he was in Saint Brigid's house in Kildare. She, as you know, had different sides to her face: one side was that of a beautiful woman and the other was that of a plain, house-keeping woman. She was at her loom, and as she wove she sang this rann, turning the beautiful side of her face to Saint Patrick:

145

"The shroud that I am weaving,
So goodly, white and seemly,
Over thee and me shall be,
And over Colum-cille."

"That must mean," said Malcolm MacCuilim slyly, "that the bodies of Patrick and Brigid were moved over to Iona."

"If you think so," said Manus O'Donnell, "I will give you another rann." And he repeated:

Honor Iona has
Of him, and Derry, love,
And Down where Patrick is
And Brigid, holds the Dove.

So that you won't be wondering how his body comes to be in Downpatrick, I will tell you that part of the history before you stir hand or foot.

"His body was buried by his monks—that was in Iona, of course. Afterwards a fleet of raiders came to the island. They were Vikings. They plundered the graves, searching for treasure that might have been left with the dead. The coffin of Colum-cille they took out of its tomb and put on the ship of a raider whose name was Mandar. They expected to find within this coffin a casket of silver inclosing the dead. They opened it. But there was no silver there, only the body that was wondrously undecayed. They closed the coffin again and flung it into the sea. And though Mandar's ship was far from Ireland when this was done the coffin floated through many channels and much open sea and reached an Irish shore. And where the Abbot of Down was walking it was washed up. He had the coffin brought to him. Then he was at the tomb of Saint Patrick and Saint Brigid beside his monastery. And he had the coffin opened there, and behold! the dead within it had a writing under his hand. And by that writing the Abbot knew that the body was Colum-cille's, and he had it buried in the tomb that is Patrick's and Brigid's."

E. MacKinstry 1935

"The story is a good one, shanachie," said Malcolm MacCui-lim, "and I shall remember it."

The first of the pilgrims, a man from Britain, had come up to them.

"It is better to remember the words that were in the writing," Manus O'Donnell said.

"What were they?"

" 'Let there be peace in perpetuity between the men of Eirin and the men of Alba'—peace and fellowship he would say now between all peoples."

"Between all peoples, peace and fellowship," the three pilgrims to Glen Colum-cille said.

The song that they heard was that of a wren in the furze near by, and the three looked up to watch a crane flying overhead.

AUTHOR'S NOTE

I ASK myself what I know about happenings in Europe during the century which Columba's life so nearly fills (500–600 A.D.; he was born 521 and died 597), and I find that for me there are hardly any landmarks. I imagine that most casual readers of history are as dubious about this particular period as I discover myself to be. It is the darkest of dark ages for us, and this because we have such scanty information as to what was taking place west and north of Italy. Only a few landmarks are familiar to us. But let us take stock of them.

Rome was taken by the Goths less than a hundred years before the opening of our century. The Roman legions were withdrawn from Britain less than sixty years before. Now the Saxons, Jutes and Angles are destroying the Roman civilization and the Christian organization in Britain. Saint Augustine will not arrive in the Kingdom of Kent until toward the end of our century. The conversion of Germany is nearly two hundred years off, and the north of Europe is still ferociously Pagan. But Clovis has been baptized, and the Frankish-Catholic state that is to be France has come into existence. Rome, captured by the Goths, threatened by the Huns, captured again by the Vandals, has ceased to be a center of imperial power. The Papacy, still connected with the Roman Empire of the East, holds back the forces of dissolution and puts order here and there. It has undertaken the great mission of the evangelization of the West. And the instrument most potent for that undertaking has appeared—the European monastic movement as inaugurated by Saint Benedict. The monasteries that are to provide a shelter for the new European culture, for Christianity, are being built in the West and the North. In the East a great civilization is still in being: Justinian the law-giver and architect is Emperor in Constantinople: for a brief while he unites Italy with the Empire of the East and puts the Popes in a favorable position.

So much for our landmarks. Now at the side of Europe farthest from Justinian's Byzantium the first faint stirrings of a new European culture may be noted. They are in Ireland, a country that Roman organization had never been set up in and that Latin letters and language had been brought to as part of the Christian offering. He who brought them, Patrick, had been a captive taken from a Roman town in Britain. Escaped, he had returned as a missionary, having prepared himself in monastic settlements on the Continent, at Tours and the island of Lerins. About seventy years before the opening of our century he had come to Ireland.

An unwritten Celtic literature had been fertilized by this late-come Latin element and the result was a distinctive and permanent contribution to the European imagination. "In Ireland alone," writes Christopher Dawson, "the native culture met the Latin tradition on relatively equal terms and it was there that the synthesis of the two elements was achieved which resulted in the formation of a vernacular Christian literature and culture." This synthesis was transmitted to Northumbria through the successors of Columba, and the Anglo-Saxons in turn transmitted it to Germany. Christopher Dawson notes that in this literature there is an unexpected combination. "Though it was essentially monastic, its interests were not confined to ecclesiastical literature. We owe to it the preservation of the heroic epic traditions, not only in Ireland, but also in England, with Beowulf and Waldere, and in Germany, where it was a monk of Fulda who saved for us the only remaining relic of the old German heroic poetry, the Hildebrandsleid." [1]

It is this union of the ecclesiastical and the national, of the monastic and the heroic, that gives such character and variety to Co-

[1] *Mediæval Religion and Other Essays.*

lumba's legend. He must have been one of the men to whom this crossing was due. Descended from the King whose raid into Britain brought about Patrick's captivity, the Pagan and heroic tradition must have been a proud and living one to him. He belonged to the guild of poets who perpetuated the secular tradition. One of his masters was Gemman, a lay teacher. His legend reflects the period of that fortunate crossing of ecclesiastical and national elements, the period of the inauguration of that vernacular culture which "infused new life into the continental church and the decadent classical civilization and was one of the main formative influences in the development of Carolingian culture." And so we have the Pagan hero, Finn, prophesying his birth; we have Mongan, the reincarnation of the sea-god Mananaun MacLir, receiving baptism at his hands; we have his friendship with the Irish Druids (but not any friendship with the Druids in the land he goes to evangelize); we have his helpfulness in the recovery of the epic of Pagan Ireland. But the monastic element is not absent from his legend, and like the other mediæval saints, precursors of Saint Francis, Columba has his animal associates—his cat, his crane, his wren.

The culture that Columba was so representative of was imaginative and literary; it had practically no influence on the political life of his country; it gave no help toward the consolidation of kingly power in Ireland and did little to foster a political national consciousness. On the Continent the great monastic foundations were a help in the creation of the political state. But the attitude of Columba toward the ruler who bore the title of High-king of Ireland was aloof or inimical. The Irish king, unlike Clovis and his successors, was unable to use the monastic establishments for the increase of his revenues, prestige or power. This was, to a large extent, due to the intensely local character of Irish social organization: the monasteries and the religious orders had to conform to that character. But to some extent it was due to the fact that Saint Patrick had unwittingly deprived the titular head of the Irish kingdoms of an advantage which Clovis and his successors were to have: the apostle's important foundation was far outside the High-king's jurisdiction. Patrick had fixed his metropolis in the north, in Armagh, while the seat of royal power was in the middle of the country, at Tara. He had been captive in the north at a time when the prestige of Emain Macha (Armagh) though fading was still impressive. Tara was the rising power and the headship of the kingdoms was going to it. Had Patrick understood this and placed his metropolis near the High-king's seat there would have been a concentration of interests that should have favored the rise of a really dominant kingship.

Columba's immediate family, sprung from the founder of the High-kingship, Niall, was now the great power in the north, in Ulster. It had divided into two dynastic families: the Kinel-Connal, later known as O'Donnells, were the immediate relations of the saint and ruled the principality of Tir-Connal; the Kinel-Owen, later known as O'Neills, ruled the richer principality of Tir-Owen, the modern Tyrone. In Columba's time there was an Irish expansion and his kinsmen were leaders in it. They had founded a kingdom across the sea from Ulster, Dalriada, the modern Argyll. Gradually they were to prevail over the Picts and the Angles and their territory was to expand into the Kingdom of Scotland. In Columba's time his cousin, Connal, was ruler of this newly founded kingdom, and it may be presumed that this prince directed the missionary to Iona.

The personality and career of Columba was so remarkable that a legend incorporating many elements—history, miracle, hero-lore —grew around his life at a very early stage. Seventy years after his death his successor in Iona, Adamnan, wrote a life of him in Latin. It is really legend, for though written as a memoir in obvious good faith, it accepts miraculous happenings and attaches to Columba's life bits of heroic tradition. Another Life was written in Old Irish. Then in the sixteenth century the legend was given its most voluminous form by a prince of Tir-Connal, Manus O'Donnell, who had scholars collect for him all that had been set down about Columba in Latin and Irish and all the poetry attributed to him. It is from this work, Betha Colaim Chille, that the present book is largely drawn.

The Irish Fellowship Club of Chicago did themselves proud when they helped to produce in an Irish Foundation Series, and through the University of Illinois, Manus O'Donnell's work. As a mere piece of publishing it is magnificent. It is a book of five hundred pages, half of them being the mediæval Irish text. It was edited and the translation made by two distinguished scholars, Father O'Kelleher and Miss Gertrude Schoepperle. Part of this text had already been edited and translated by Dr. Henebry. But it is to the work of Father O'Kelleher and the late Mrs. Schoepperle Loomis that whatever fullness and continuity that are in the present work are due.

Of course the legend as given in Manus O'Donnell's text had to be treated very freely. Just as in the Latin and the Old Irish Lives certain interests were being served, so in Manus O'Donnell's Life there is partisanship. It was written to glorify the descendants of Connal Gulban and especially the Kinel-Connal who had a feud with the Kinel-Owen. The present writer's interest was to present Columba as the rich and vivid personality that can be discerned in all versions of the legend and in all poems attributed to him; the Gael of all time, impetuous, generous, winning; the champion of the oppressed in an age of barbarism, the holder of the Christian ideal, the creator of a small piece of civilization in Europe's dark age. To project this figure much rearrangement and many omissions had to be made. Then, too, O'Donnell's work has not the continuity that we look for in a biography: the events of Columba's life are related under the headings of Visions, Labors, Journeys, Prophecies and so on, and the chronological order is not clear. To give the narrative the order of a man's life and to project the personality a narrative had to be composed out of the elements that Manus O'Donnell had brought together.

This Manus O'Donnell is an interesting figure in Irish political history. About the time that he succeeded his father as Prince of Tir-Connal, Henry the Eighth of England had decided on a states-man-like policy as regards the country in which his power was more nominal than real. He discountenanced a war of conquest in Ireland and he wanted the Irish magnates to give some token of recognition to the English Crown. He was willing to appoint as deputy, not some personage of his own court, but one of the magnates them-selves. Had this policy been put into operation Ireland would have been left in the possession of the Gaelic and Norman-Irish lords with one of their number having the chance of getting the whole force of the country behind him. Manus O'Donnell, apparently, was one of the magnates who was willing to coöperate in the working of this policy. Unfortunately Henry was forced to pick for his deputy, not the type that the situation demanded, a steady man with an imper-sonal ambition, but an unsteady and personal-minded man, the head of the Norman-Irish house of Kildare, Fitzgerald. He made a false move, aroused the anger of Henry, and was committed to the Tower. Then his son dashed round the country in an effort to get the magnates to make war on the Crown with his own youthful self as leader. Something portentous happened: the Fitzgerald castle was taken by artillery. A great weapon had come into the hands of the Crown, and the magnates could be reached in their castles and chastised.

The statesman-like temper that Henry had shown ended then. He resolved on the destruction of the greatest of the Irish houses— the Kildare Fitzgeralds who were descended from the first Norman barons in Ireland and who were connected by marriage with the chief Gaelic families. They were warred upon, executed, attainted. Certain Gaelic princes, O'Donnell amongst them, tried to reëstablish them and were defeated. The English court now saw that they had the Irish magnates in their grasp, and the land-hungry English gentry looked toward baronial estates in Ireland. The scene was set for the wars of extermination that were to take place in the next reigns.

All this meant a great deal to Manus O'Donnell in his northern principality. He had entered into alliance with the Kinel-Owen; the descendants of Connal Gulban were in amity with each other for a while. He hoped for a Geraldine restoration. The MacCarthys, who had the most prosperous of the principalities, had taken the heir of the Fitzgeralds under their protection: Manus O'Donnell took a wife from this southern family, the Lady Eleanor MacCarthy. This marriage caused consternation amongst the English in Ireland; they saw in it a first move toward a new league amongst the magnates, Gaelic and Norman-Irish.

But the English Crown, whose policy was to become more and more savage, prevailed. O'Donnell and O'Neill suffered defeat. The descendants of Connal Gulban had both to accept the gold chain which made them vassals to the English Crown. They exchanged their principalities for earldoms. "They have given for the earldom of Ulster the kingdom submissively and unwisely," a despairing Irish poet cried.

Manus O'Donnell had finished his Life of Columba before these events had taken place. When we remember that "the grey foreign gun" that so anguished the poet whose line we have quoted, had come into use, and that the Renaissance had reached England and France, we are amazed that any great lord in Western Europe could be so mediæval-minded as the writer of Betha Colaim Chille shows himself to be. He died in 1563, and that great summary of Irish history, written under the protection of the remnants of his family, *The Annals of the Four Masters,* gives us this to remember him by. "Benign, amiable, bountiful and hospitable man toward the learned, the destitute, the poets and the ollavs . . . a learned man, skilled in many arts, gifted with profound intellect and knowledge of every science, died on 9th. Feb. at his mansion-seat at Lifford, a castle which he had erected in despite of O'Neill and the Kinel-Owen, and was interred in the burial-place of his predecessors, successors and ancestors at Donegal, in the monastery of Saint Francis, after having vanquished the Devil and the World." So let us leave Manus O'Donnell. He was not one of the princes who read Ariosto: instead he set his scribes and scholars to "put into Gaelic the part of the Life that was in Latin, and make easy the part that was hard Gaelic." And by doing this he bequeathed to us a mediæval story which is not meager as is the typical mediæval legend, but voluminous and varied, and which reflects an earlier period, the pre-Carolingian period in Europe, at the moment when the tide was turning from barbarism toward civilization.

PADRAIC COLUM